THE KID'S BOOK OF BIBLE ACTIVITIES

VOLUME 2

Vickie Save

Illustrated by
Ken Save

BARBOUR
PUBLISHING, INC.
Uhrichsville, Ohio

© MCMXCIX by Barbour Publishing, Inc.

ISBN 1-57748-612-9

Unless otherwise noted, Scripture used is from the Authorized King James Version of the Bible.

Scriptures marked (NIV) are taken from the HOLY BIBLE: NEW INTERNATIONAL VERSION ®. NIV ®. Copyright © 1973, 1978, 1984 by International Bible Society. Used by permission of Zondervan Publishing House. All rights reserved.

Published by Barbour Publishing, Inc., P.O. Box 719, Uhrichsville, Ohio 44683
http://www.barbourbooks.com

Member of the
Evangelical Christian
Publishers Association

Printed in the United States of America.

WORDSEARCH

```
I  D  L  J  G  Q  P  A  N  G  E  L
G  J  A  I  L  I  U  T  K  P  W  U
A  O  N  X  H  D  S  L  A  V  E  C
D  H  D  S  A  O  G  E  B  O  T  R
H  Z  R  Z  D  L  R  T  I  R  X  F
P  O  M  N  G  S  C  T  A  B  Q  V
W  T  Y  J  U  D  G  E  M  E  N  T
M  C  S  J  O  E  H  R  Y  I  F  K
W  O  H  L  B  Y  A  S  T  O  R  M
V  I  S  I  O  N  E  F  J  S  E  V
```

JUDGEMENT   IDOLS

JOY   VISION

HEART   SLAVE

LETTERS   ANGEL

JAIL   STORM

WORSHIP   GOD

WORDSEARCH

```
B T W I E L D E R S D A J
I G J A H T N I Y N H O C
V E E T H I O P I A N Z P
H N R V P C Z F U P Y I B
G T U S H M B X G S L X Q
O I S T G R J Q S I W D C
Q L A L S T E P H E N B F
N E L D O C W P A J E M G
D P E A N T I O C H A K D
K U M E Z F S T O N I N G
J V D L U T H E L R Y K R
E M F K F I W S X N H J E
```

SEEK   ELDERS
STEPHEN   STONING
PHILIP   ANTIOCH
ETHIOPIAN   DEATH
JEWISH   GENTILE
JERUSALEM   FIND

WORDSEARCH

```
K X C S P E E C H T F S V M
A D P Q T B E L I E V E R S
Q R B F M A R C Z K A W R
A P C O Y I A U P V X L O
N C E B P E N T E C O S T
W J T S G F K J T S B G L
L I D Y S G R A C E T Y W D
R L Y A Y O Z P R A Y E R
O L H U I U C S G U T H Q
H Q J E L P N H I Z M X L N
H E A V E N V E C H U R C H
```

HOLYSPIRIT   BELIEVERS
HEAVEN   APOSTLE
PENTECOST   GRACE
PETER   SPEECH
ACTS   CHURCH
PRAYER   SAUL

WORDSEARCH

```
R T B L V H I U L O N S O
Q H E A L S B A I L M A D
V P F M Z A N H S H J L W
C K I T P R N Y T R U T H
M G L A E T C I L Y B H P
L P O T N B A P T I S M G
O D E G K F S T A F G Z E
V F Q W X J F Y I L M H K
E Q S A L V A T I O N C T
I T E R T W D X E J N Q V
```

SALVATION   FAITH
BAPTISM   LIFE
WAY   TEMPTATION
HEALS   ETERNAL
TRUTH   SALT
LIGHT   LOVE

WORDSEARCH

H	W	F	A	T	H	E	R	T	E	O
E	Y	K	L	R	K	V	B	S	O	C
M	J	X	I	U	S	C	L	X	M	F
L	A	S	L	A	U	E	W	N	Y	D
R	M	T	K	V	P	J	G	L	D	J
H	E	S	T	S	U	A	O	Y	B	E
B	S	G	O	H	J	H	D	H	P	S
F	Z	G	C	N	E	T	Z	I	N	U
Q	M	A	R	K	P	W	M	A	J	S
G	D	T	R	I	N	I	T	Y	Q	N

HOLY   JOHN

SON   GOSPELS

LUKE   FATHER

MATTHEW   MARK

JAMES   TRINITY

GOD   JESUS

SEARCH FOR IT
FIND THE NAMES OF THE FOUR GOSPELS BELOW.
(HINT: THE FIRST FOUR BOOKS OF THE NEW TESTAMENT ARE CALLED THE GOSPELS.)

```
N U J R L D O E M O B K
K L A J O N T F C U M S
R M D X N L H I G D A Z
T J M A T T H E W E R J
L K I C S P A L N H K Q
E U D I A R K G O B O M
M F K X W G C J G Q E A
L A H E N P B Y A M Q R
W N T I J O H N P M Y B
F Z J T H V F C B Y P H
```

_____   _____

_____   _____

WORDSEARCH

```
B U E S T H E R T P H R Y
Q E A M R E Z E K I E L C
T P S A L M S G J Z D L H
S M L N E H E M I A H S R
F O D O Z C F L S Y B C O
I G L A R H E J I R M X N
J P X O A U A V E S O I I
S K N I M R B V W K H Q C
B N A F N O O B D Q K A L
O S I H J R N H G B V L E
I T C E P W Z P K I N G S
```

NEHEMIAH	ESTHER
ELISHA	EZRA
JOB	ISAIAH
SOLOMON	PROVERBS
PSALMS	CHRONICLES
KINGS	EZEKIEL

WORDSEARCH

```
B I M Y H Q L X T R I A L S F
G F A I T H V D N R O M O J P
R C O S G P F Q C W U C R U C
S A W A B C S H A L D T D E E
H E A R T I D A V I D N H O C
E W S E R P J K L X B V E G A
P R A I S E P I V M P G U Z I
H E Z R N J E B A E U F Q S G
E R Q E L N I T M F G T D O H
R V D U R D E N E S Y N K N B
D S J P F H Z R K X M O T G T
```

HEART   REFUGE
TRUTH   TRIALS
SINNER   SONG
PSALM   PRAISE
SHEPHERD   LORD
DAVID   FAITH

WORDSEARCH

```
L O M J S A M U E L U E
A E X O D U S B Y O S R
N W V F S R A L T Z J G
U J G I I E O D N L T E
M U R U T H S K D Q P N
B D E H Y I B S U M I E
E G P X S M C A V C W S
R E C J O S H U A F V I
S S A G Q L N L S H K S
```

SAUL	EXODUS
GENESIS	JOSHUA
LEVITICUS	SAMUEL
RUTH	NUMBERS
JUDGES	MOSES

WORDSEARCH

```
K I N G X J N C L J Q R
A C H I J O R D A N O S
P R O M I S E J I K D H
M U T P N H B S G N O E
V D R I A U B V A A C B
C O V E N A N T R R F R
H L A W S E S A A M Q E
B U S H W T H F Y G K W
T D F Z E P B O E P L S
```

JOSHUA
JORDAN
SIN
COVENANT
PROMISE
STANDS

KING
LAWS
REST
HEBREWS
BUSH
PHARAOH

GOD'S PROMISE

GOD HAS GIVEN ABRAM A NEW NAME THAT MEANS FATHER OF NATIONS. HE HAS PROMISED ABRAM A SON.

CROSS OUT EVERY LETTER THAT APPEARS FOUR TIMES— WRITE THE REMAING LETTERS IN ORDER TO FIND HIS NEW NAME.

C P A D L W E S I

F Y T G I B Q G Q

W E S K Q F Q C Y

R L Y P A W Y K G

K T H C D T S D I

S F K P E T A W G

C L D M E L P F I

WHAT IS HIS NEW NAME ? _____

WORDSEARCH

```
I D S P C G A K M V U O D K S N H
O H O L Y S P I R I T D P I E K P
U D Y W O C W M X Z X B T D R J M
G T R F N X E O I J B E R W P N J
Q R B I H Y A L R T Q A B A E H S
T E L O Z A B P F D G J Z Q N P F
N E D E N G P Y K F L H N I T O D
J Q E X A W V N J U A K W L R J W
G L Y S H Q K T E M P T E D S I C
F D E V A R Z Y C W L H B C T G H
A S X K W N Q O D U N G M O B T Q
B D S E R V G M Z R V D B T R I W
S R A C J C U E Z A Q T R A U M L
E D T M N X V P L F A G E F Y L V
M T D C R E A T I O N H X S V U G
L R Y E O Z U F M Y C H K F T N I
```

ADAM

ANGEL

CREATION

HOLY SPIRIT

SWORD

EARTH

TREE

EVE

SERPENT

TEMPTED

GARDEN

EDEN

WORDSEARCH

```
X L O B N Z U N F J A Z T U Y F
B M Z A D O C K I M H L O R D A
O R H B P F V X G L K Y D I G L
L T O A K N A W O H T Y C A N S
A C W D B H U T C G B F M H D M
S E M O E A X U H J W I S D O M
F O C Q B A T T L E A P Q L Z G
J K L X D Z B H J V R V A K N R
H W O O R B G Q S O M S W I R I
K D Y U M S E A W H B A K F Q E
E G A J C O L F I A E I G L M F
Q V L P T S N Z K P N B N Y U H
P M A R R I E S H T X E A S R I
```

BATHSHEBA	ABSALOM
URIAH	FATHER
MARRIES	LOYAL
LORD	BATTLE
NATHAN	KING
GRIEF	ZADOCK
SOLOMON	WISDOM

WORDSEARCH

```
C I P L H O S P T S A G
Q A F A T Z F D E R W H
K E D R L G P N M I R V
Q U B M J A R G P J N I
J H S K E V C K L X J M
E T W G M B W E E P O H
R D L R P N S A F Z N U
U C A X W U A N K Q A J
S Q A N O I N T E D T B
A D H H G Y U M H I H Y
L N E B C E L W O A A O
E T L T O A R K D P N U
M V J E V Y D X F M C Z
```

WEEP   JERUSALEM
DANGER   PALACE
ARMY   ARK
JONATHAN   TEMPLE
ANOINTED   NATHAN
JUDAH   HOUSE

FIND THE WORDS

T	M	H	Q	C	Y	S	S	R	O	A	H
B	S	F	L	N	O	V	D	T	C	T	I
W	O	G	A	L	I	L	E	E	I	X	U
J	L	T	E	H	J	R	G	A	X	D	M
N	D	G	F	A	E	N	F	O	C	F	I
U	I	K	P	S	I	V	R	H	L	S	J
M	E	D	G	L	A	T	K	Q	T	F	A
O	R	N	A	C	R	O	M	A	N	Y	I
W	U	E	B	G	X	K	O	D	Z	B	R
R	H	Q	I	L	T	B	E	P	J	N	U
J	I	S	R	A	E	L	M	H	V	W	S

ROMAN   JAIRUS

FAITH   HEALING

GALILEE   SOLDIER

BOAT   ISRAEL

FIND THE WORDS

P	S	D	O	N	L	Q	A	C	F	Z	K
G	N	P	J	E	S	U	S	T	N	M	R
O	J	G	U	L	I	C	Y	H	B	E	B
D	H	F	S	V	O	C	O	O	T	Z	A
S	O	D	L	C	A	J	P	S	D	O	P
T	M	V	R	G	N	S	L	S	Y	S	T
Q	L	A	E	A	F	Y	T	Q	P	P	I
N	V	Q	D	N	J	C	D	N	E	I	Z
C	T	R	S	S	A	V	I	O	U	R	E
F	O	W	R	H	S	T	E	C	X	I	G
J	P	D	K	Z	D	M	I	T	W	T	I

JESUS   BAPTIZE
SPIRIT   GOD
JOHN   SAVIOUR
JORDAN   DOVE

FIND THE WORDS

```
C D S A U L H L P H G
S A M U E L I E W X I
R N F A I T H K A R A
D R R P D A V I D R N
R S L I N G Q N U F T
L J A E V I M G B O K
P B E T H L E H E M L
H C J F G O L I A T H
A B A R M O U R D P G
```

SAUL	HEART
ISRAEL	GOLIATH
KING	GIANT
SAMUEL	ARMOUR
BETHLEHEM	SLING
DAVID	FAITH

CONNECT THE DOTS

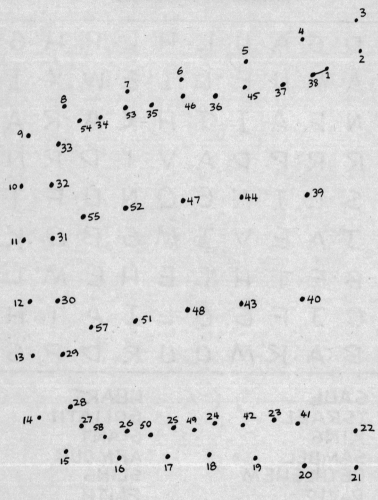

CONNECT THE DOTS

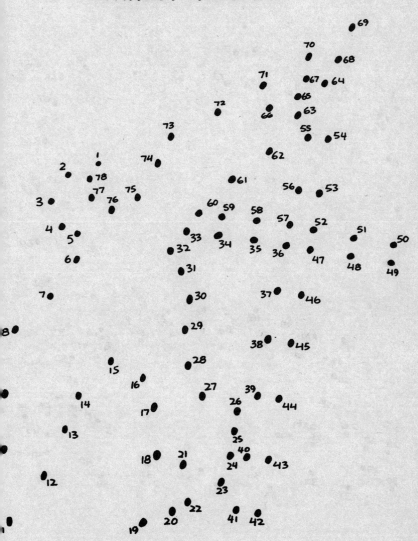

CONNECT THE DOTS

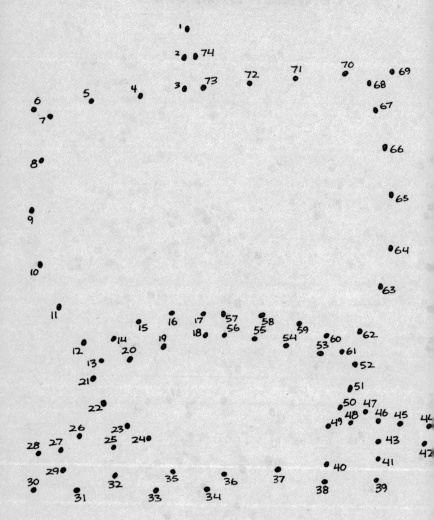

CONNECT THE DOTS

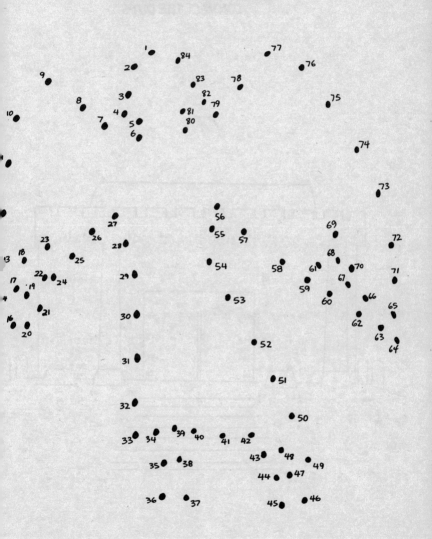

HELP BUILD THE TEMPLE
CONNECT THE DOTS

CONNECT THE DOTS

YOUNG DAVID WENT TO BATTLE AGAINST--?

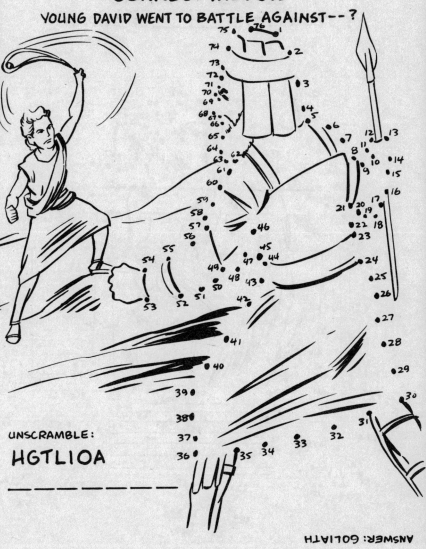

UNSCRAMBLE:

HGTLIOA

_ _ _ _ _ _ _

CONNECT THE DOTS

JESUS , THE _____ OF JUDAH !

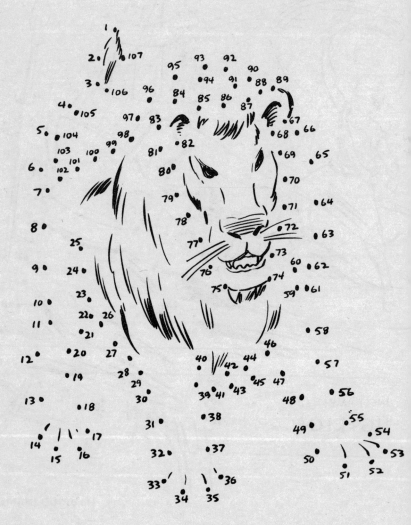

CONNECT THE DOTS
PETER WALKS ON THE WATER

CONNECT THE DOTS

JESUS HAD RIDDEN INTO JERUSALEM ON THIS ANIMAL

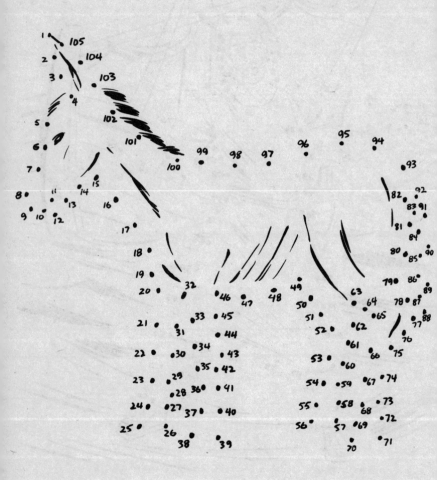

CONNECT THE DOTS

SAUL MET JESUS ON THE ROAD TO DAMASCUS.

GOD CREATED A BEAUTIFUL GARDEN FOR ADAM AND EVE TO LIVE IN. THE SERPENT TEMPTED THEM TO DISOBEY GOD. WHICH TREE DID THEY EAT FROM WHEN THEY SINNED?

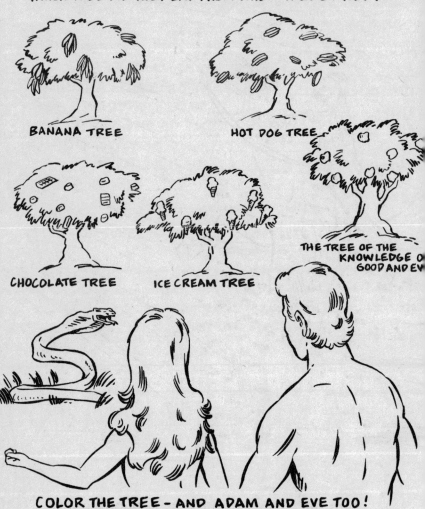

BANANA TREE

HOT DOG TREE

CHOCOLATE TREE

ICE CREAM TREE

THE TREE OF THE KNOWLEDGE O GOOD AND EV

COLOR THE TREE - AND ADAM AND EVE TOO!

ANSWER: THE TREE OF THE KNOWLEDGE OF GOOD AND EVIL.

SOLVE THE PUZZLE AND COLOR THE PICTURE

GOD GAVE A PROMISE TO NEVER DESTROY THE WORLD AGAIN
BY WATER. WHAT SIGN DID HE GIVE OF HIS PROMISE?
USE THE CIRCLED LETTERS TO FIND THE ANSWERS.

NOAH BUILT AN _ _O_ _ .

_ _O_ _ WAS THE ONLY GOOD MAN LEFT.

IT WOULD _ _ _O_ FOR FORTY DAYS AND NIGHTS.

THE _O_ _ _ _ _ CAME IN TWO BY TWO.

THE _O_ _ IS THE FRONT OF THE BOAT.

GOD_ _ _O_ _ _ _ _ TO SAVE NOAH.

NOAH OPENED A _ _ _ _ _ _O TO SEND
OUT A DOVE.

O O O O O O O

ANSWERS: ARK, NOAH, RAIN, ANIMALS, BOW, PROMISED, WINDOW
(RAINBOW)

THE TOWER OF BABEL

PEOPLE BUILT A HIGH TOWER TO PROVE HOW POWERFUL AND SMART THEY WERE — BUT GOD WAS NOT PLEASED.

UNSCRAMBLE THE WORDS AND PUT THEM IN PROPER ORDER TO FIND OUT WHAT GOD DID TO STOP THEM.

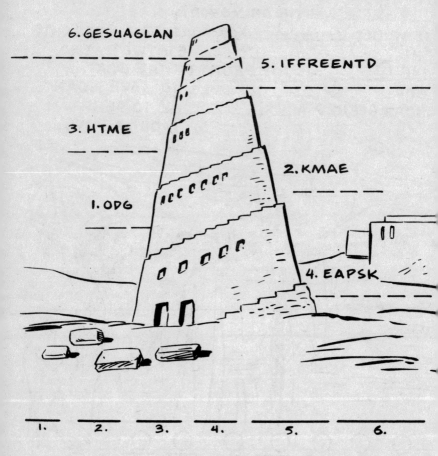

6. GESUAGLAN

5. IFFREENTD

3. HTME

2. KMAE

1. ODG

4. EAPSK

1. _____ 2. _____ 3. _____ 4. _____ 5. _____ 6. _____

WHATEVER HAPPENED TO JOSEPH?

USING THE CODE BELOW, FIND THE ANSWER.

A	B	C	D	E	F	G	H	I	J	K	L	M
26	25	24	23	22	21	20	19	18	17	16	15	14

N	O	P	Q	R	S	T	U	V	W	X	Y	Z
13	12	11	10	9	8	7	6	5	4	3	2	1

7 12 8 22 11   19   4 26 8   25 15 22 8 8 22 23

25 2   20 12 23   26 13 23   14 26 23 22   26

9 6 15 22 9   18 13   22 20 2 11 7 .

UNSCRAMBLE THE LETTERS BELOW TO FIND THE NAME OF:

THE SEVENTH BOOK OF THE BIBLE:

SJEUGD

— — — — — — —

THE EIGHTH BOOK OF THE BIBLE:

HRTU

— — — —

THE NINTH BOOK OF THE BIBLE:

LSEA 1 UM

— — — — — — — —

THE TENTH BOOK OF THE BIBLE:

LM 2 USAE

— — — — — — — —

LOOK IN YOUR BIBLE

GOD REVEALED HIS NAME TO MOSES. WHAT WAS GOD'S NAME ?

LOOK UP EXODUS 3: 13-14. (NIV)

ANSWER:_____

ANSWER: "I AM WHO I AM."

USE THE CODE BELOW TO ANSWER THE QUESTIONS.

A B C D E F G H I J K L M
26 25 24 23 22 21 20 19 18 17 16 15 14

N O P Q R S T U V W X Y Z
13 12 11 10 9 8 7 6 5 4 3 2 1

THE NEXT BOOK IN THE
BIBLE AFTER EXODUS IS:

___ ___ ___ ___ ___ ___ ___ ___ ___
15 22 5   18 7   18 24 6

THIS MEANS:

___ ___ ___ ___ ___   ___ ___ ___
26 25 12 6   7   7   19 22

___ ___ ___ ___ ___ ___ ___
15 22 5   18 7   22 8

THE LEVITES ARE:
                    9
___ ___ ___ ___
20 12 23 8

___ ___ ___ ___ ___ ___ ___
11 9   18 22 8   7

LEVITICUS HELPS THE PEOPLE LIVE:

___ ___ ___ ___   ___ ___ ___ ___ ___
19 12 15 2   15 18 5   22 8

UNSCRAMBLE THE LETTERS BELOW TO NAME
THIS BOOK OF THE BIBLE

(IT'S A HARD ONE, SO YOU GET A LITTLE HELP ON THIS.)

Y D M E O U N T O E R

_ E _ _ _ E _ E _ O _ O _ _

HOW MANY YEARS WERE THE ISRAELITES
IN THE DESERT?

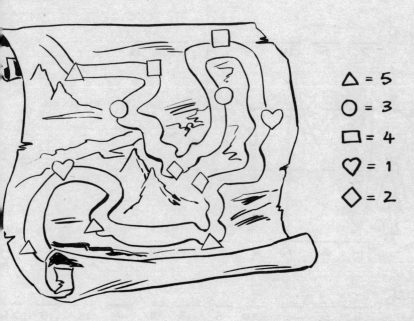

△ = 5

O = 3

□ = 4

♡ = 1

◇ = 2

_ + □ + O + ◇ + O + □ + ♡ + ◇ + △ + △ + ♡ + △ = ___

ANSWER: ____ YEARS

USE THE CODE BELOW TO NAME THE FIRST FIVE BOOKS OF THE BIBLE.

A	B	C	D	E	F	G	H	I	J	K	L	M
1	2	3	4	5	6	7	8	9	10	11	12	13

N	O	P	Q	R	S	T	U	V	W	X	Y	Z
14	15	16	17	18	19	20	21	22	23	24	25	26

1. __ __ __ __ __ __ __
   7 5 14 5 19 9 19

2. __ __ __ __ __ __
   5 24 15 4 21 19

3. __ __ __ __ __ __ __ __ __
   12 5 22 9 20 9 3 21 19

4. __ __ __ __ __ __ __
   14 21 13 2 5 18 19

5. __ __ __ __ __ __ __ __ __ __ __
   4 5 21 20 5 18 15 14 15 13 25

USE THE CODE BELOW TO ANSWER THE QUESTIONS.

A	B	C	D	E	F	G	H	I	J	K	L	M
26	25	24	23	22	21	20	19	18	17	16	15	14

N	O	P	Q	R	S	T	U	V	W	X	Y	Z
13	12	11	10	9	8	7	6	5	4	3	2	1

WHO SHOWED HIMSELF TO MOSES IN THE BURNING BUSH?

__ __ __ __ __ __ __ __ __ __ __ __ __ __
19 22 26 13 20 22 15 12 21 7 19 22 15 12 9 23

WHO IS THE ANGEL OF THE LORD?

__ __ __ __ __
    22 8 6 8

WHO IS JESUS?

__ __ __
   12 23

UNSCRAMBLE THE LETTERS
OF THESE BOOKS OF THE BIBLE

CTUSLEIVI Ⓞ _ _ _ Ⓞ _ _ _ _

YONEUTERDMO Ⓞ _ _ _ _ _ _ _ _ _ _

DJGUES _ _ Ⓞ _ _ _

1KGINS _ _ _ _ Ⓞ

NSIGK 2 _ _ _ _ _ _

NSICOECHRL _ _ _ _ _ _ _ _ Ⓞ _

AERZ _ _ _ Ⓞ

HNAEIHME Ⓞ _ _ _ _ _ _ . _

REESHT _ _ Ⓞ _ _ _ _

OJB _ _ _

SPMSLA _ _ Ⓞ _ Ⓞ

SPBRREVO _ _ _ _ Ⓞ _ _ _

PUT THE CIRCLED LETTERS IN THE RIGHT ORDER.
YOU'LL FIND THESE BOOKS OF THE BIBLE IN THE:

Ⓞ Ⓞ Ⓞ Ⓞ Ⓞ Ⓞ Ⓞ Ⓞ Ⓞ Ⓞ Ⓞ Ⓞ

USE THE CODE BELOW TO ANSWER THE QUESTIONS.

A B C D E F G H I J K L M
26 25 24 23 22 21 20 19 18 17 16 15 14

N O P Q R S T U V W X Y Z
13 12 11 10 9 8 7 6 5 4 3 2 1

NAME THE BOOK THAT COMES
AFTER PSALMS.

$\overline{}$ $\overline{9}$ $\overline{12}$ $\overline{5}$ $\overline{22}$ $\overline{9}$ $\overline{25}$ $\overline{8}$

WHO WROTE MOST OF THE
BOOK OF PROVERBS?

$\overline{}$ $\overline{18}$ $\overline{13}$ $\overline{20}$

$\overline{}$ $\overline{12}$ $\overline{15}$ $\overline{12}$ $\overline{14}$ $\overline{12}$ $\overline{13}$

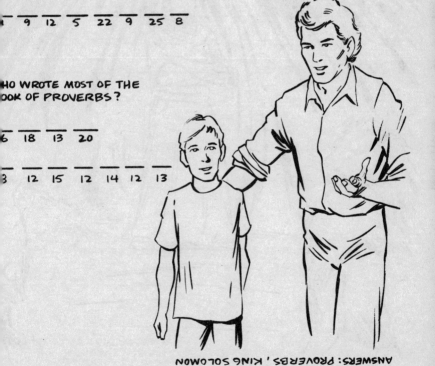

LOOK IN YOUR BIBLE
LOOKS LIKE DANIEL IS IN A LOT OF DANGER !
FIND OUT WHAT HAPPENS -- THEN COLOR THE PICTURE.

READ DANIEL 6:1-24.

THESE THREE WERE PUT INTO A FIERY FURNACE BY KING NEBUCHADNEZZAR — BUT THEY WEREN'T EVEN SINGED!

WHO WERE THEY? USE THE CODE BELOW TO FIND OUT.

A B C D E F
1 2 3 4 5 6
G H I J K L
7 8 9 10 11 12
M N O P Q R
13 14 15 16 17 18
S T U V
19 20 21 22
W X Y Z
23 24 25 26

__ __ __ __ __ __ __ __ ,
19 8 1 4 18 1 3 8

__ __ __ __ __ __ __ AND __ __ __ __ __ __ __ __
13 5 19 8 1 3 8   1 2 5 4 14 5 7 15

(GOOD LUCK PRONOUNCING THESE!!)

ANSWERS: SHADRACH, MESHACH, ABEDNEGO

WHAT IS A PSALM?

CROSS OUT EVERY LETTER THAT APPEARS FOUR TIMES IN THE PUZZLE. COPY THE REST OF THE LETTERS, IN ORDER, TO FIND THE ANSWER.

A D S P F C
F C P D O A
C N A C F D
P D F A G P

A PSALM IS A _____ .

READ PSALM 23, THEN
DRAW YOURSELF INTO
THE PICTURE

SOLVE THE PUZZLE

_ESSE   DAVID'S FATHER
1

PHILISTIN_S   ISRAEL'S ENEMY
2

_AUL   KING OF ISRAEL
3

M_SIC   DAVID USES THIS TO COMFORT SAUL
4

_AMUEL   GOD'S PROPHET
5

_SRAEL   GOD'S NATION
6

_ONS OF JESSE   DAVID'S BROTHERS
7

_ORD   GOD
8

G_LIATH   GIANT PHILISTINE
9

WA_   ISRAEL FIGHTS
10

_AVID   GOD'S NEW KING
11

WHAT DOES IT SAY?

‾1‾ ‾2‾ ‾3‾ ‾4‾ ‾5‾ ‾6‾ ‾7‾ ‾8‾ ‾9‾ ‾10‾ ‾11‾

WORD JUMBLE

HOW DAVID FLED FROM JERUSALEM

ON HIS ☐☐☐☐☐

USE THE CODE BELOW TO FIND THE NAMES OF JESUS'
EARTHLY PARENTS.

A	B	C	D	E	F	G
26	25	24	23	22	21	20

H	I	J	K	L	M	N
19	18	17	16	15	14	13

O	P	Q	R	S	T	U
12	11	10	9	8	7	6

V	W	X	Y	Z
5	4	3	2	1

‾14‾ ‾26‾ ‾9‾ ‾2‾

AND

‾17‾ ‾12‾ ‾8‾ ‾22‾ ‾11‾ ‾19‾

JESUS AT THE TEMPLE

HOW OLD WAS JESUS THE FIRST TIME HE WENT
TO THE TEMPLE? LOOK AT THE NUMBERED BRICKS,
AND SOLVE THE QUESTION BELOW.

☐ + ▭ + ▭ + △ + ◇ + ▭ + ◇ + ▭ = _____

CHECK LUKE 2:41-52 TO MAKE SURE YOU HAVE THE RIGHT ANSWER

USE THE CODE BELOW TO FIND OUT WHAT JESUS
SAID TO DRIVE AWAY SATAN'S TEMPTATIONS

IT IS WRITTEN!

A B C D E F G
1 2 3 4 5 6 7

H I J K L M N
8 9 10 11 12 13 14

O P Q R S T U
15 16 17 18 19 20 21

V W X Y Z
22 23 24 25 26

1. $\overline{13}$ $\overline{1}$ $\overline{14}$ $\overline{4}$ $\overline{15}$ $\overline{5}$ $\overline{19}$ $\overline{14}$ $\overline{15}$ $\overline{20}$ $\overline{12}$ $\overline{9}$ $\overline{22}$ $\overline{5}$ $\overline{15}$ $\overline{14}$

$\overline{2}$ $\overline{18}$ $\overline{5}$ $\overline{1}$ $\overline{4}$ $\overline{1}$ $\overline{12}$ $\overline{15}$ $\overline{14}$ $\overline{5}$

2. $\overline{4}$ $\overline{15}$ $\overline{14}$ $\overline{15}$ $\overline{20}$ $\overline{16}$ $\overline{21}$ $\overline{20}$ $\overline{20}$ $\overline{8}$ $\overline{5}$ $\overline{12}$ $\overline{15}$ $\overline{18}$ $\overline{4}$ $\overline{25}$ $\overline{15}$ $\overline{21}$ $\overline{18}$

$\overline{7}$ $\overline{15}$ $\overline{4}$ $\overline{20}$ $\overline{15}$ $\overline{20}$ $\overline{8}$ $\overline{5}$ $\overline{20}$ $\overline{5}$ $\overline{19}$ $\overline{20}$

3. $\overline{23}$ $\overline{15}$ $\overline{18}$ $\overline{19}$ $\overline{8}$ $\overline{9}$ $\overline{16}$ $\overline{20}$ $\overline{8}$ $\overline{5}$ $\overline{12}$ $\overline{15}$ $\overline{18}$ $\overline{4}$ $\overline{25}$ $\overline{15}$ $\overline{21}$ $\overline{18}$

(NIV) $\overline{7}$ $\overline{15}$ $\overline{4}$ $\overline{1}$ $\overline{14}$ $\overline{4}$ $\overline{19}$ $\overline{5}$ $\overline{18}$ $\overline{22}$ $\overline{5}$ $\overline{8}$ $\overline{9}$ $\overline{13}$ $\overline{15}$ $\overline{14}$ $\overline{12}$ $\overline{25}$

ANSWERS: 1. MAN DOES NOT LIVE ON BREAD ALONE. 2. DO NOT PUT THE LORD YOUR GOD TO THE TEST. 3. WORSHIP THE LORD YOUR GOD, AND SERVE HIM ONLY.

JESUS HAS A MESSAGE FOR YOU.

UNSCRAMBLE THE WORDS, THEN PUT THE LETTERS IN THE MATCHING SHAPES BELOW.

SJESU   __ ♡ __ __ __

HTTRU   __ __ ☆ __ __

YWA   __ __ ⬡

ELIF   __ □ __ __

NSI   __ __ __

YHOL   __ △ ○ __

EVLO   __ __ ◇ __

DLRO   __ △ __

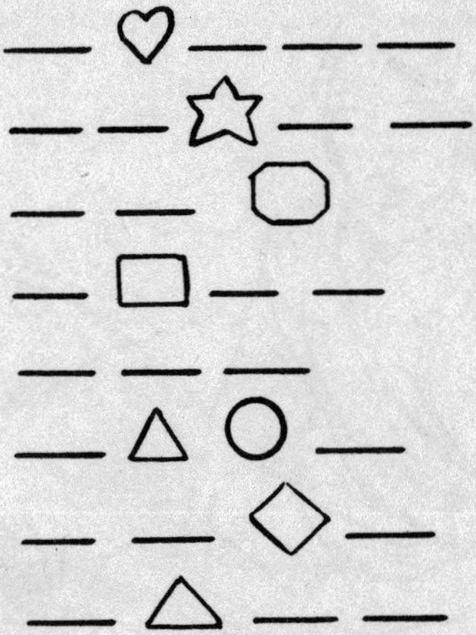

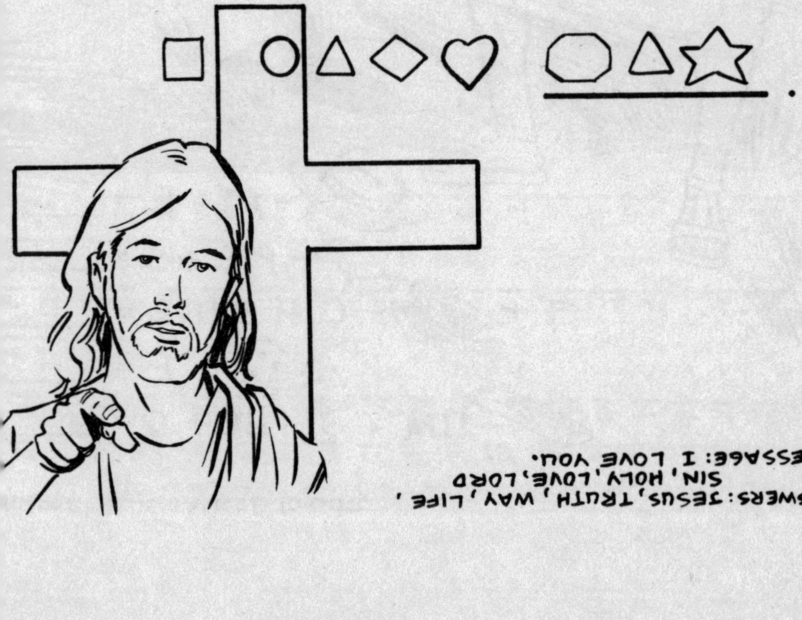

□ ○ △ ◇ ♡   ⬡ △ ☆ .

WHAT'S JESUS DOING?

ADD OR SUBTRACT THE PICTURE CLUES AND LETTERS
ACCORDING TO THE + OR — SIGNS TO FIND THE ANSWER.

— AT + E = _____

— P, G + S = _____

T + _____ — C, H + ING = _____

_____ — E = _____

— UM + 1 — NE + D = _____

UNSCRAMBLE THE LETTERS TO FIND OUT THE
NAMES OF SOME OF JESUS' DISCIPLES.
(HINT: LOOK UP MATTHEW 10:2-4.)

LIPPHI _____

STHOAM _____

MAJSE _____

THRABOOLMEW _____

NSMIO _____

SUJDA _____

TRPEE _____

NJHO _____

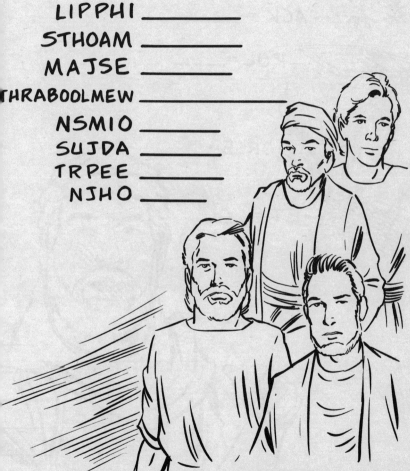

WHO THOUGHT HE WAS JESUS' FAVORITE DISCIPLE?

ADD AND SUBTRACT THE PICTURE CLUES AND LETTERS.

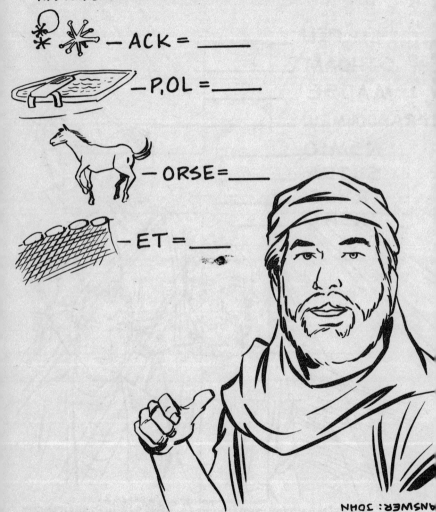

— ACK = _____

— P,OL = _____

— ORSE = _____

— ET = _____

USE THE CODE BELOW TO FIND THE NAMES OF THE THREE
PERSONS OF THE TRINITY.

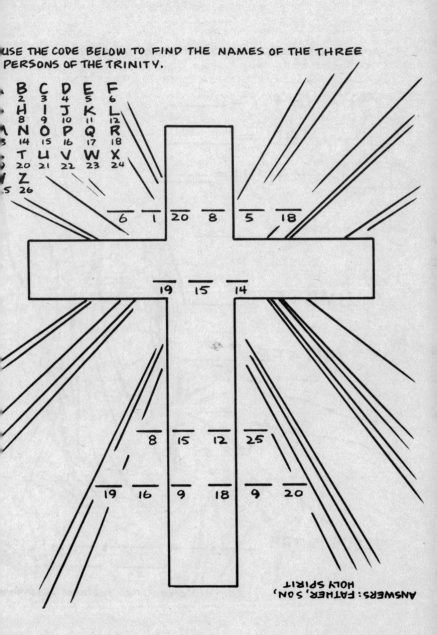

	B	C	D	E	F
	2	3	4	5	6
	H	I	J	K	L
	8	9	10	11	12
N	O	P	Q	R
14	15	16	17	18
T	U	V	W	X
20	21	22	23	24
Z
26

—— —— —— —— —— ——
6   1   20   8   5   18

—— —— ——
19   15   14

—— —— —— ——
8   15   12   25

—— —— —— —— —— ——
19   16   9   18   9   20

ADD OR SUBTRACT THE PICTURE CLUES AND LETTERS.

– VE + Y = _____

– IMBL = _____

– CK + TH = _____

– H = _____

– UMB + E = _____

– GHT + FE = _____

JESUS IS THE _____ , _____ _____ , _____ _____ !

USING THE CODE BELOW, FIND THE ANSWERS AND FINISH
THE SENTENCES.

A	B	C	D	E	F	G	H	I	J	K	L	M
26	25	24	23	22	21	20	19	18	17	16	15	14

N	O	P	Q	R	S	T	U	V	W	X	Y	Z
13	12	11	10	9	8	7	6	5	4	3	2	1

THE BOOK OF ACTS TELLS WHAT HAPPENED TO $\underline{}_{17}\ \underline{}_{22}\ \underline{}_{8}\ \underline{}_{6}\ \underline{}_{8}$ '
$\underline{}_{21}\ \underline{}_{12}\ \underline{}_{15}\ \underline{}_{15}\ \underline{}_{12}\ \underline{}_{4}\ \underline{}_{22}\ \underline{}_{9}\ \underline{}_{8}$ AFTER HIS RESURRECTION.

PETER WAS USED BY GOD TO $\underline{}_{25}\ \underline{}_{6}\ \underline{}_{18}\ \underline{}_{15}\ \underline{}_{23}\ \underline{}_{7}\ \underline{}_{19}\ \underline{}_{22}$
$\underline{}_{24}\ \underline{}_{19}\ \underline{}_{6}\ \underline{}_{9}\ \underline{}_{24}\ \underline{}_{19}$.

THE $\underline{}_{20}\ \underline{}_{12}\ \underline{}_{8}\ \underline{}_{11}\ \underline{}_{22}\ \underline{}_{15}\ \underline{}_{12}\ \underline{}_{21}\ \underline{}_{24}\ \underline{}_{19}\ \underline{}_{9}\ \underline{}_{18}\ \underline{}_{8}\ \underline{}_{7}$
SPREAD ALL OVER THE WORLD.

ANSWERS: JESUS, FOLLOWERS, BUILD THE CHURCH, GOSPEL OF CHRIST

UNSCRAMBLE THE WORDS

LAPU _____

NVOIIS _____

KSEE _____

RLEETT _____

HJSEIW _____

LJIA _____

ADD OR SUBTRACT THE PICTURE
CLUES AND LETTERS.

IN THE BOOK OF ACTS, SAUL'S NAME WAS CHANGED TO

— IG = ____

— PPLE = ____

— SA, CER = ____

— BIB, E = ____

DID YOU KNOW?
ADD OR SUBTRACT THE PICTURE CLUES AND LETTERS.

– T + SUS = _____

– M,CE + S = _____

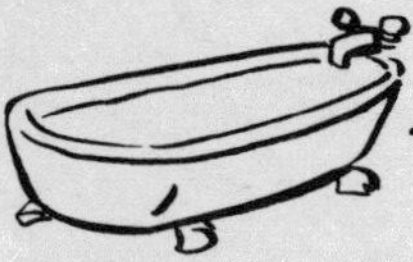

– BA + E = _____

– UN +  – C,R,W = _____

– F = _____

G + 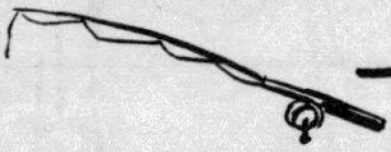 – R = _____

ANSWER: JESUS IS THE SON OF GOD.

MATCH THE COLUMNS.

ANGEL

SPEAR

BRIDLE

TOUNGES OF
FIRE

CHAINS

SLING

ARK

MATCH THE COLUMNS

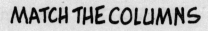

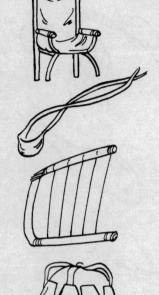

HARP

CROWN

THRONE

ARMOR

SLING

SWORD

MATCH THE COLUMNS

THORNS

PALM BRANCH

PIG

COLT

THE WORD

MATCH THE COLUMNS

PYRAMID

PALM TRE

HELMET

SWORD

CLOAK

MATCH THE COLUMNS

STAFF

WATER JUG

FISHING BOAT

NET

SANDAL

ANGEL

PAUL'S MISSIONARY JOURNEY
HELP PAUL GET TO HIS DESTINATION OF ROME.

JESUS WAS ARRESTED IN THE GARDEN OF
GETHSEMANE. PETER TRIED TO GET AWAY FROM
THE SOLDIERS. HELP HIM FIND HIS WAY OUT.

EXIT

ADD THE NUMBERS TO FIND OUT HOW MANY DAYS JESUS WAS IN THE DESERT.

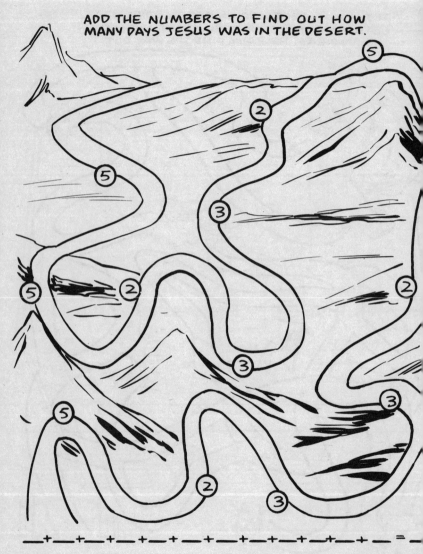

___ + ___ + ___ + ___ + ___ + ___ + ___ + ___ + ___ + ___ + ___ + ___ = ___

AS YOU GO THROUGH THE MAZE, PICK UP EACH LETTER AND FIND THE
ONLY WAY WE GET TO HEAVEN.

BY BELIEVING AND TRUSTING
: _____ ALONE !

MANY PATHS THAT LEAD NOWHERE - ONLY ONE SURE WAY.
CAN YOU FIND IT?

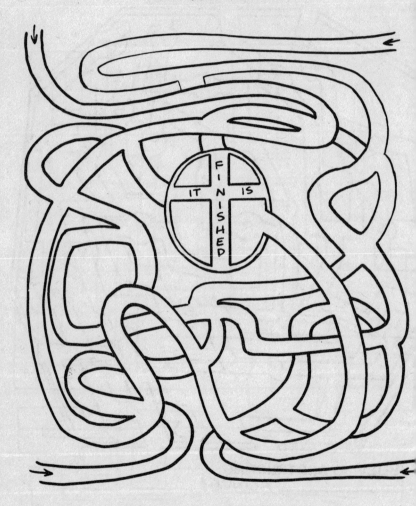

ANIEL AND THE ISRAELITES WERE TAKEN AS PRISONERS
F WAR TO BABYLON – A BIG AND BUSY CITY.
ELP DANIEL FIND HIS NEW APARTMENT.

HELP THE ISRAELITES GET TO THE PROMISED LAND.

JOSEPH WAS SOLD AS A SLAVE BY HIS BROTHERS AND
TAKEN TO EGYPT. HELP THE CARAVAN GET THROUGH
THE DUNES AND AROUND THE DANGERS.

HELP DAVID ESCAPE SAUL

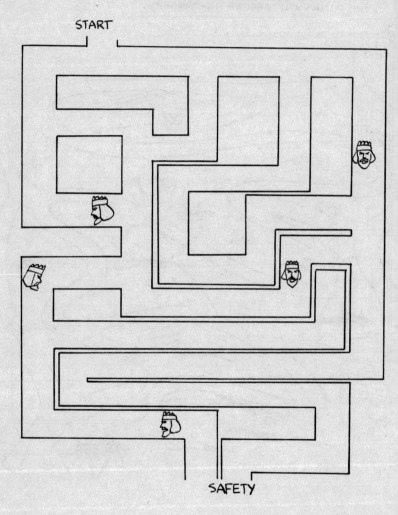

START

SAFETY

HELP DAVID GET OUT OF JERUSALEM

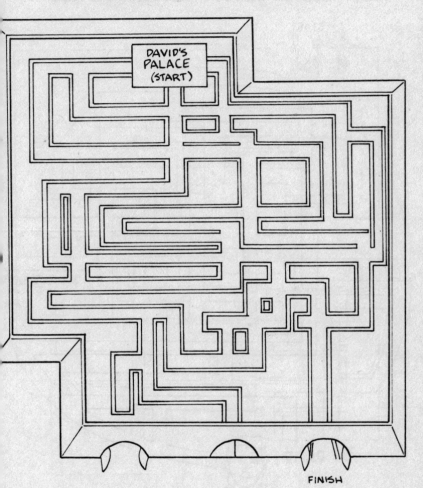

DAVID'S PALACE (START)

FINISH

HELP SAMUEL FIND THE SON OF JESSE THAT GOD HAS CHOSEN

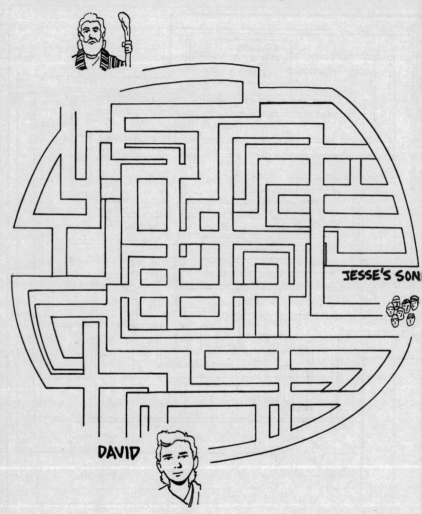

ON TO JERUSALEM!

START

FINISH

HELP JOSEPH, MARY AND JESUS FIND THE WAY TO EGYPT

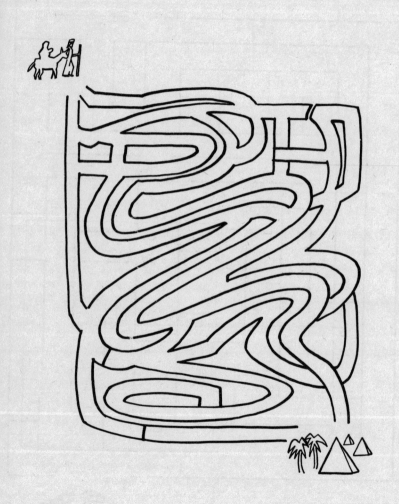

HOW TO DRAW DAVID

START WITH SIMPLE SHAPES

DRAW GUIDELINES LIGHTLY

DRAW DETAILS

FINISH AND ERASE GUIDELINES

NOW- TRY ON YOUR OWN PIECE OF PAPER!

HOW TO DRAW JESUS

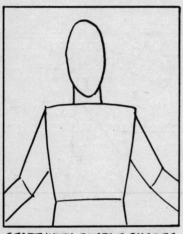

START WITH SIMPLE SHAPES

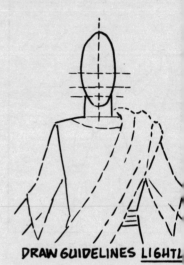

DRAW GUIDELINES **LIGHTL**

ADD DETAILS: EYES, NOSE
MOUTH, EARS, BEARD,
HAIR AND CLOTHING

FINISH AND ERASE GUIDELIN

NOAH BUILT THE ARK

PUT THE PICTURES IN ORDER AS THEY HAPPENED FIRST, SECOND, THIRD AND LAST. WRITE THE CORRECT NUMBER IN THE BLANK SPACE UNDER EACH PICTURE.

#_____

#_____

#_____

#_____

ANSWER: 3, 2, 1, 4

JOSEPH WAS GIVEN A COAT OF MANY COLORS.
USE THE COLOR GUIDE BELOW TO COLOR IT YOURSELF.

RED   2= YELLOW   3= BLUE   4= GREEN 5=ORANGE 6=PURPLE

FIND THE DIFFERENCES

MOSES COMES DOWN THE MOUNTAIN WITH THE TEN COMMANDMENTS OF GOD. CIRCLE THE DIFFERENCES.

SNAKES IN THE DESERT

CIRCLE THE SEVEN DEADLY SNAKES.

FIND THE DIFFERENCES

FIND THE DIFFERENCES

SOLOMON'S TEMPLE

FIND AT LEAST SIX DIFFERENCES IN THE TWO PICTURES BELOW.

JESUS IN THE MANGER

WHAT'S WRONG WITH THIS PICTURE?

ZACCHEUS, A WEALTHY TAX COLLECTOR, CLIMBED A TREE
TO GET A BETTER LOOK AT JESUS. BUT, THIS IS A VERY
STRANGE TREE. FIND AND CIRCLE WHAT DOESN'T BELONG.

FIND ALL THE BREAD AND FISH

FIND THE DIFFERENCES

WHAT'S WRONG WITH THIS PICTURE?

JESUS HAD FIVE THOUSAND PEOPLE TO FEED. ONLY TWO OF THE ITEMS BELOW ARE WHAT HE USED TO MULTIPLY WITH A MIRACLE. CIRCLE WHAT BELONGS.

ANSWER: HE USED THE BREAD AND FISHES.

PETER'S GONE FISHING AND HIS NET IS FULL—BUT SOME
OF HIS CATCH, HE COULD NOT SELL AT THE FISH MARKET!
CIRCLE WHAT DOESN'T BELONG.

HELP PETER FIND HIS SHADOW.

FIND THE DIFFERENCES
PAUL ON HIS JOURNEY

HELP PAUL FIND HIS SHADOW.

DRESS DAVID FOR BATTLE

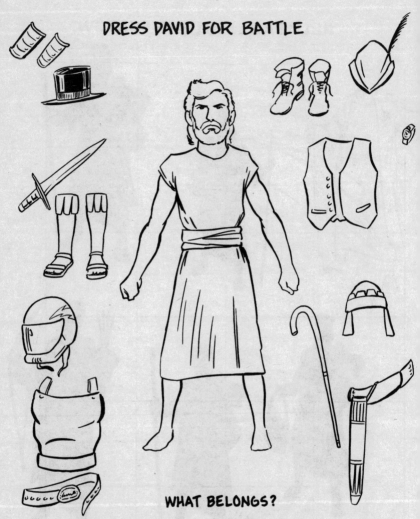

WHAT BELONGS?

CUT OUT AND GLUE OR DRAW IT ON

DRAW MOSES

USING THE LEFT SIDE AS A GUIDE, DRAW, THEN COLOR, MOSES.

FINISH THE PICTURE
THEN
LOOK IN YOUR BIBLE.

THIS MAN WITH THE JAWBONE — DO YOU KNOW WHO HE IS?

HIS NAME IS _____.

LOOK IN JUDGES 15:15-16 FOR THE ANSWER.

ANSWER: SAMSON

DRAW FOR YOURSELF

FINISH THE OTHER SIDE.

DRAW FOR YOURSELF

USING WHAT IS IN EACH SQUARE, GO TO THE FOLLOWING PAGE AND COPY THIS PICTURE.

COPY FROM THE PREVIOUS PAGE.

DRAW FOR YOURSELF

USING THE SQUARES AS A GUIDE, GO TO THE FOLLOWING PAGE
AND COPY THIS PICTURE.

COPY FROM THE PREVIOUS PAGE.

DRAW FOR YOURSELF
USING WHAT IS IN EACH SQUARE, GO TO THE FOLLOWING
PAGE AND COPY THE PICTURE.

"I STAND AT THE DOOR AND KNOCK. IF ANYONE HEARS MY VOICE AND OPENS THE
DOOR, I WILL COME IN AND EAT WITH HIM AND HE WITH ME." REVELATIONS 3:20

(NIV)

DRAW FROM THE PREVIOUS PAGE.

DRAW FOR YOURSELF

USING WHAT IS IN EACH SQUARE, GO TO THE FOLLOWING PAGE AND COPY THE PICTURE.

DRAW FROM THE PREVIOUS PAGE.

COLOR BY NUMBER

JESUS ALWAYS TOOK TIME TO PRAY

1 = FLESH TONE 2 = BLUE 3 = BROWN 4 = LIGHT BLUE
5 = LIGHT BROWN 6 = GREEN 7 = YELLOW 8 = DARK GREEN
9 = GREY

FINISH THE PICTURE
JESUS DIED ON A CROSS FOR OUR SINS.

FINISH THE PICTURE

THEN COLOR.

ADAM & EVE

ACROSS

1) THE _____ GUARDED THE GATE TO THE GARDEN.
2) IN SHAME, ADAM AND EVE _____ FROM GOD.
3) _____ WAS SECOND TO EAT THE FORBIDDEN FRUIT.
4) AFTER SINNING, ADAM AND EVE WERE SENT _____ OF THE GARDEN.
5) THE _____ TEMPTED EVE TO EAT THE FRUIT (SNAKE).

DOWN

1) ADAM NAMED THE _____.
3) EVE _____ THE FORBIDDEN FRUIT.
6) ADAM AND EVE WERE NOT TO EAT THE _____ OF THE TREE IN THE MIDDLE OF THE GARDEN.
7) THE SERPENT _____ TO EVE (DID NOT TELL THE TRUTH).

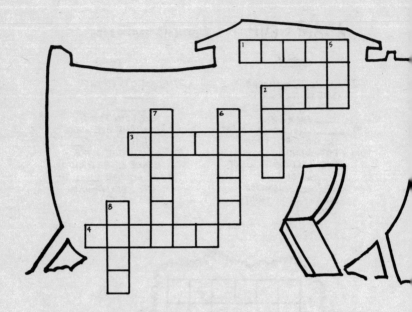

NOAH'S FAMILY BUILDS THE ARK

GENESIS 6:9 - 7:5

ACROSS

1) GOD SAID TO SEAL THE WOOD WITH _____.

2) NOAH'S SON

3) NOAH'S NEIGHBORS _____ AT NOAH AND HIS ARK.

4) GOD SAID TO USE THIS KIND OF WOOD TO BUILD THE ARK.

DOWN

2) NOT FRONT OR BACK, BUT _____

5) NOAH'S SON

6) THE ARK WAS _____ STORIES TALL INSIDE.

7) NOAH'S SON

8) GOD TOLD _____ HOW BIG TO BUILD THE ARK.

NOAH'S JOURNEY

GENESIS 7

ACROSS

1) WATER FALLING FROM THE SKY

2) GOD SAVED NOAH AND ALL HIS _____.

3) GOD SHUT THE _____ OF THE ARK.

4) THE DOVE CAME BACK TO NOAH WITH AN ____ BRANCH.

5) _____ COVERED ALL THE EARTH DURING THE FLOOD.

DOWN

1) GOD SET A _____ IN THE SKY AS A SIGN OF HIS PROMISE.

2) IT RAINED FOR _____ DAYS AND NIGHTS.

6) A BIRD NOAH SENT OUT FROM THE ARK – RHYMES WITH "LOVE"

ABRAM'S JOURNEY GENESIS 11:31 - 13:4

ACROSS

1) ABRAM'S WIFE

2) ABRAM'S FATHER

3) ABRAM AND HIS FAMILY JOURNEYED TO A FAR-AWAY _____.

DOWN

4) ABRAM LEFT THE CHALDEAN CITY OF ___.

5) SARAI'S HUSBAND.

6) FALSE GODS.

7) ABRAM'S FAMILY LIVED IN _____ FOR SHELTER AS THEY JOURNEYED.

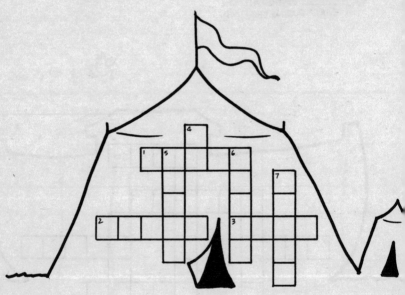

GOD'S COVENANT
WITH
ABRAHAM

GENESIS 15:1-18

ACROSS

1) GOD MADE A _____ TO GIVE ABRAM A SON.

2) ABRAM HAD NO _____.

DOWN

3) ABRAM LOVED ___ AND PROMISED TO SERVE HIM.

4) THE MANY LIGHTS IN THE NIGHT SKY.

5) ABRAM WAS NOW AN ___ MAN, NOT YOUNG.

6) GOD WOULD GIVE ABRAM AND SARAI A _____.

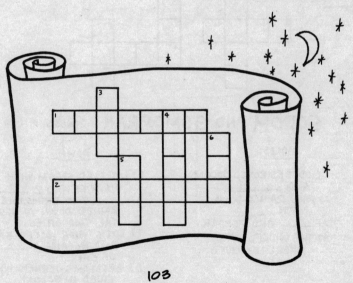

SODOM AND GOMORRAH GENESIS 19:1-30

ACROSS

1) GOD DESTROYED SODOM AND _____.
2) FIRE RAINED DOWN WITH _____.
3) _____ AND PEPPER.
4) THE WICKED CITY WHERE LOT LIVED.

DOWN

5) LOT FLED SODOM WITH HIS WIFE AND 2 _____.
6) _____ AND BRIMSTONE RAINED DOWN TO DESTROY THE TWO CITIES.
7) LOT'S WIFE LOOKED BACK AND BECAME A _____ OF SALT.
8) ABRAHAM'S NEPHEW WHO LIVED IN SODOM.

ISAAC'S BIRTH

GENESIS 21:1-8

ACROSS

1) THE SOUND OF LAUGHING.

2) ABRAHAM AND SARAH'S SON.

3) TALK TO GOD.

DOWN

4) ABRAHAM WAS 100 WHEN ISAAC WAS BORN. SARAH WAS ALSO VERY _____.

5) ISAAC GOT BIGGER. HE _____.

6) GOD _____ HIS PROMISES.

7) ISAAC'S MOTHER.

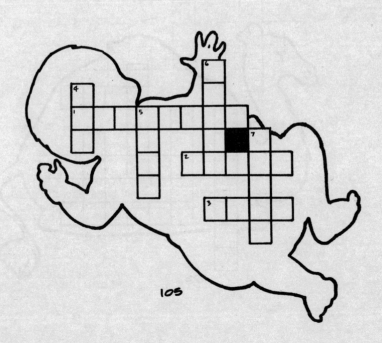

105

ISAAC'S BRIDE

GENESIS 24

ACROSS

1) ABRAHAM'S SERVANT GAVE REBEKAH A _____ TO WEAR ON HER FINGER...

2) ...AND 2 GOLD _____ TO WEAR ON HER WRISTS.

3) REBEKAH GAVE WATER TO THESE HUMP-BACKED ANIMALS.

DOWN

4) ISAAC'S WIFE.

5) ABRAHAM'S SON.

6) NEWLY MARRIED WOMAN. "HERE COMES THE _____."

7) REBEKAH DREW WATER FROM THE _____.

106

JACOB'S DREAM

GENESIS 28:10-16

ACROSS

1) A VISION DURING SLEEP
2) ROCK
3) GOD'S HEAVENLY MESSENGERS
4) WHAT YOU REST YOUR HEAD ON AT NIGHT AS YOU SLEEP.
5) GOD TOLD JACOB HE WOULD GIVE HIM THE _____ HE WAS LYING ON.
6) KIDS

DOWN

2) WHAT WE DO WHEN WE ARE TIRED AT NIGHT
7) HIGH DWELLING PLACE OF GOD
8) USED TO STEP UP ON TO REACH HIGH PLACES
9) FIRST–_____, BAND_____, HELP.

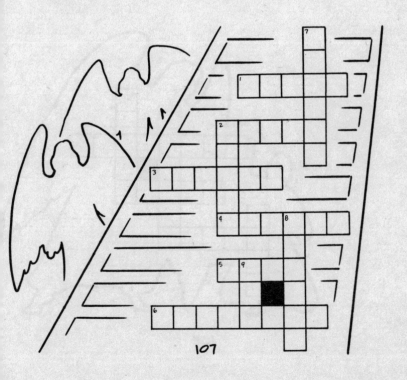

107

JACOB WRESTLES THE ANGEL

GENESIS 32:24-31

ACROSS

1) THE GRACE BEFORE A MEAL

2) TO STRETCH OUT FOR SOMETHING

3) A MESSENGER OF GOD.

DOWN

4) THE ANGEL TOUCHED JACOB'S _____.

5) JACOB'S NEW NAME

6) DAYBREAK, SUNRISE

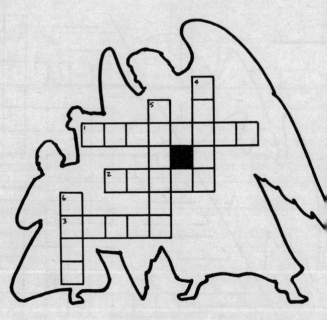

JOSEPH'S TROUBLE

GENESIS 37:15-35

ACROSS

1) JOSEPH'S OLDER BROTHER WHO TRIED TO PROTECT HIM

2) WHAT FLOWS THROUGH OUR VEINS

3) JOSEPH'S BROTHERS SOLD HIM AS A _____.

4) A LARGE, DEEP HOLE IN THE GROUND

5) JACOB WAS VERY ____ TO HEAR THAT HIS SON WAS DEAD.

DOWN

6) JOSEPH HAD ELEVEN _____.

7) TO LET SOMETHING FALL - RHYMES WITH "CROP"

8) JOSEPH AND HIS BROTHERS TENDED THEIR FATHER'S _____ OF SHEEP.

PHARAOH'S DREAM

GENESIS 41

ACROSS

1) A VISION DURING SLEEP

2) KING OF EGYPT

3) THE NUMBER AFTER "SIX"

4) IN WHAT MANNER?
   RHYMES WITH "COW"

5) OPPOSITE OF OUT

6) OVERWEIGHT

DOWN

5) NOT A HE, NOT A SHE, BUT AN ___

7) OPPOSITE OF POOR

8) OPPOSITE OF QUESTION

9) UNDERWEIGHT
   RHYMES WITH "PIN"

10) A CEREAL CROP, SUCH
    AS WHEAT. RHYMES
    WITH "TRAIN"

11) PLURAL OF FEMALE
    CATTLE

110

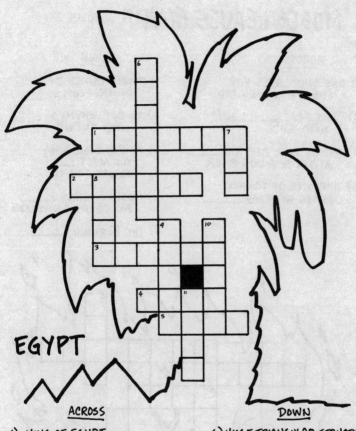

EGYPT

ACROSS

1) KING OF EGYPT

2) HUGE SCULPTURE OF A LION WITH A MAN'S FACE

3) A FALSE IMAGE OF WATER IN THE DESERT

4) THE MIGHTY _____ RIVER FLOWS THROUGH EGYPT.

5) THE DESERT HAS _____ DUNES

DOWN

6) HUGE TRIANGULAR STRUCTURE

7) OPPOSITE OF COLD

8) _____ TREE, RHYMES WITH "CALM"

9) A PLACE OF SHADE AND WATER IN THE DESERT

10) THE NUMBER AFTER SIX

11) A BABY SHEEP

MOSES LEAVES EGYPT EXODUS 2:11

ACROSS

1) ONE WHO CARES FOR SHEEP AS MOSES DID

2) "LET MY _____ GO!", SAID GOD.

3) MOSES TOOK OFF HIS _____ AT THE BURNING BUSH.

8) OPPOSITE OF TOWARD - MOSES WENT FAR _____.

DOWN

1) PEOPLE OWNED BY OTHER PEOPLE

4) TO CUT, RHYMES WITH "NEW"

5) TO BUY SOMETHING YOU MUST _____ MONEY FOR IT.

6) MOSES ANGRILY _____ AN EGYPTIAN (KILLED).

7) THE BURNING _____

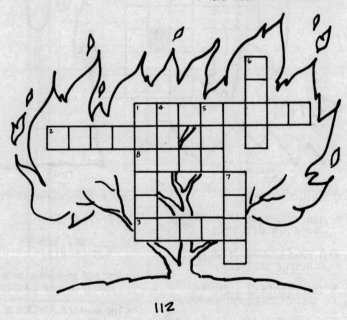

112

PASSOVER

EXODUS 12:1-36

ACROSS

1) A BABY SHEEP
2) THE ISRAELITES LEFT EGYPT QUICKLY, IN _____
3) THEY ATE _____ HERBS WITH THEIR PASSOVER MEAL.
4) ONE TIME
5) THE ISRAELITES PUT _____ ON THEIR DOORPOSTS AS A SIGN FOR DEATH TO PASS BY THAT HOUSE.

DOWN

6) GOD SPARED THE FIRST-BORN OF THE HEBREWS ON THE NIGHT OF _____.
7) THE ISRAELITES ATE UNLEAVENED _____.
8) YOU MUST _____ RAW MEAT. RHYMES WITH "BOOK"

113

THE RED SEA

EXODUS 14

ACROSS

1) TWO-WHEELED WAR WAGONS DRAWN BY SWIFT HORSES

2) THE PEOPLE CROSSED THE RED SEA ON _____ LAND.

3) GOD _____ THE ISRAELITES FROM PHARAOH. RHYMES WITH "PAVED"

DOWN

4) PHARAOH'S GREAT _____ OF MEN AND CHARIOTS WAS DESTROYED.

5) THE RED _____

6) WALLS OF _____ WERE ON BOTH SIDES OF THE PEOPLE AS THEY CROSSED THE SEA ON DRY LAND.

WATER FROM THE ROCK

EXODUS 17:1-7

ACROSS

1) GOD TOLD MOSES TO ____ THE ROCK. RHYMES WITH "PIT"

2) THE MAN GOD CHOSE TO LEAD HIS PEOPLE FROM EGYPT

3) IF YOU ARE THIRSTY, HAVE SOMETHING TO ____.

4) OPPOSITE OF IN

DOWN

5) GOD'S PEOPLE WERE ____ WITHOUT WATER TO DRINK

6) WATER CAME OUT OF THE ____ AFTER MOSES HIT IT.

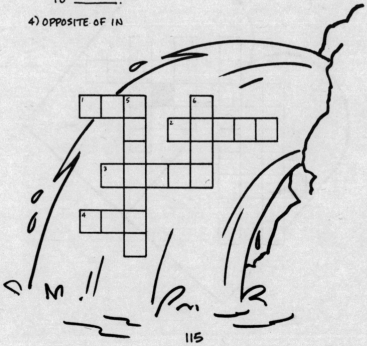

THE TEN COMMANDMENTS EXODUS 20:1-17

ACROSS

1) FALSE GODS

2) TO TAKE FROM SOMEONE
   WITHOUT PERMISSION

3) OPPOSITE OF TRUTH

4) DO NOT USE GOD'S
   NAME IN _____.
   (RHYMES WITH "RAIN")

DOWN

2) KEEP THE _____ DAY

5) THERE IS ONLY ____ GOD.

6) "THOU SHALL NOT _____."

7) "THOU SHALL NOT _____
   THY NEIGHBOR'S GOODS."

8) "_____ THY MOTHER AND
   FATHER."

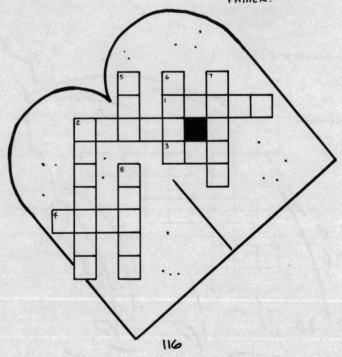

116

THE
TABERNACLE
EXODUS 25, 26

ACROSS

1) THE COLOR OF THE SKY

2) LARGE PIECES OF CLOTH HUNG AROUND THE TABERNACLE

3) A BRIDE WEARS THIS OVER HER FACE, THE CURTAIN BEFORE THE HOLY OF HOLIES.

4) THE LAMPS BURNED _____.

5) _____ OF THE COVENANT

DOWN

6) COLOR OF GRAPE SODA COLOR OF ROYALTY

7) SACRIFICES WERE BURNED ON AN _____.

8) PRECIOUS YELLOW METAL

9) BURNS OIL FOR LIGHT

117

THE WILDERNESS

NUMBERS 14:20-24

ACROSS

1) MOSES MADE A BRASS _____ TO HEAL THE PEOPLE'S SNAKE BITES.

2) THE _____ ON THEIR FEET NEVER WORE OUT.

3) THE ISRAELITES SPENT _____ YEARS WANDERING IN THE WILDERNESS.

DOWN

4) A DRY BARREN LAND

5) THE PEOPLE WHINED, "WE WANT TO GO BACK TO _____."

6) THE ISRAELITES LIVED IN _____ AS THEY WANDERED.

7) THE PEOPLE'S ____ OF UNBELIEF ANGERED GOD. (RHYMES WITH "FIN")

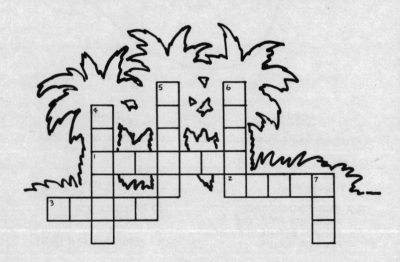

118

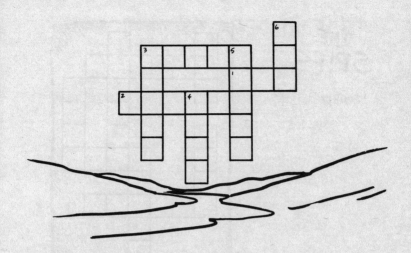

THE PROMISED LAND DEUTERONOMY 34

ACROSS

1) MOSES WAS 120 YEARS ____ WHEN HE DIED.

2) THE PEOPLE HAD TO CROSS THE _____ RIVER TO ENTER CANAAN. (STARTS WITH J, ENDS WITH N)

3) A BASEBALL MIT IS MADE TO _____ THE BALL.

DOWN

3) MOSES WAS NOT ALLOWED TO _____ THE RIVER JORDAN.

4) MOSES _____ BEFORE THE PEOPLE ENTERED THE PROMISED LAND (PASSED AWAY).

5) THE LAND WAS FLOWING WITH MILK AND _____.

6) _____ BURIED MOSES BECAUSE THE PEOPLE HAD ALL LEFT FOR THE PROMISED LAND.

THE
SPIES

JOSHUA 2

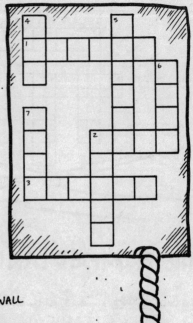

ACROSS

1) AN OPENING IN THE WALL
   TO THE OUTSIDE

2) THE SPIES PROMISED TO
   KEEP RAHAB'S FAMILY
   _____ FROM HARM.

3) RELATIVES

DOWN

2) SECRET AGENTS (RHYMES WITH "FLIES")

4) THE NUMBER THAT COMES AFTER "ONE"

5) GOD PUT _____ IN CHARGE OF THE
   PEOPLE AFTER MOSES DIED.

6) RAHAB PUT A LONG, RED _____ OUT
   HER WINDOW FOR THE SPIES TO
   CLIMB DOWN TO SAFETY.

7) THE TOP OF A HOUSE

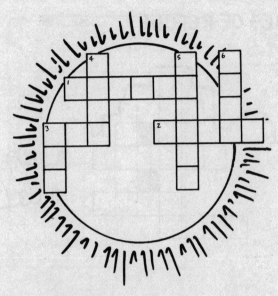

GOD FIGHTS FOR JOSHUA
AND HIS PEOPLE JOSHUA 10:8-14

ACROSS

1) THE MAN WHO LED ISRAEL
   AFTER MOSES DIED

2) THE SUN STOOD _____,
   NOT MOVING.

3) THE "LIGHT HOLDER"
   OF DAYTIME (RHYMES
   WITH "RUN")

DOWN

3) THE SPACE HIGH OVER HEAD -
   RHYMES WITH "PIE"

4) "LIGHT HOLDER" OF THE
   NIGHT (RHYMES
   WITH "SOON")

5) A FIGHT BETWEEN ARMIES

6) CHUNKS OF ICE FALLING
   FROM THE SKY
   LIKE RAIN

CITIES OF REFUGE

JOSHUA 20

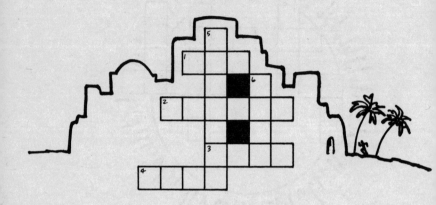

ACROSS

1) OPPOSITE OF LIVE
   RHYMES WITH "TIE"

2) LARGE TOWNS

3) TO TAKE A LIFE

4) PROTECTED FROM
   HARM

DOWN

5) AN ERROR

6) "ALIVE AND ____"
   RHYMES WITH
   "SELL"

122

JUDGES

JUDGES 3

ACROSS

1) OPPOSITE OF UP

2) GOD WOULD SEND JUDGES TO ____ HIS PEOPLE FROM THEIR ENEMIES.

3) THE PEOPLE WORSHIPED IDOLS, OR ____ GODS.

4) THE PEOPLE ____ THEIR PROMISE TO SERVE GOD AND SINNED.

DOWN

5) PLURAL OF JUDGE

6) THE PEOPLE WOULD ____ DOWN BEFORE IDOLS.

7) OPPOSITE OF YES

8) THE PEOPLE DID ____ IN THE SIGHT OF THE LORD. (WICKEDNESS)

9) OPPOSITE OF STRONG

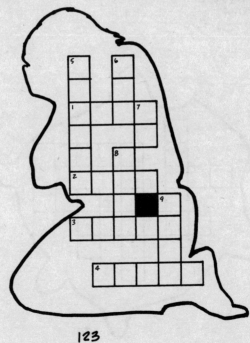

123

GIDEON

JUDGES 6

ACROSS

1) ANIMALS THAT GRAZE EAT GREEN _____.

2) AN ANGEL SPOKE TO GIDEON FROM UNDER A _____ OAK TREE. (OPPOSITE OF SMALL)

3) OPPOSITE OF WET

4) SHEEPSKIN, WOOL – RHYMES WITH "PEACE"

DOWN

1) GOD CHOSE _____ TO SAVE HIS PEOPLE FROM THE MIDIANITES.

3) WATER DROPLETS ON GRASS IN THE MORNING

5) MESSENGER OF GOD

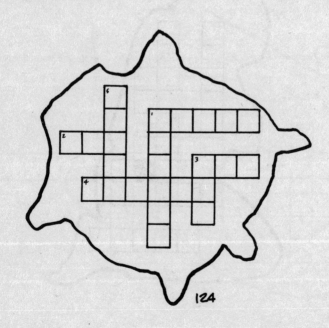

124

YOUNG SAMSON

JUDGES 13

ACROSS

1) BOY CHILD - RHYMES WITH "FUN"

2) KIDS

3) HIS LONG HAIR GAVE HIM HIS STRENGTH

DOWN

4) GOD'S MESSENGER

5) TO CUT A LITTLE - RHYMES WITH "BRIM"

6) TO SWALLOW A LIQUID

7) SAMSON'S _____ GREW LONG.

125

RUTH

ACROSS

1) BOAZ MARRIED RUTH AND SHE BECAME HIS _____.

2) RUTH _____ HER MOTHER-IN-LAW, NAOMI, WITH HER WHOLE HEART.

3) _____ FELL IN LOVE WITH RUTH AND MARRIED HER.

4) OPPOSITE OF OUT

DOWN

1) AN OWL ASKS, "_____?".

2) RUTH PROMISED TO NEVER _____ NAOMI.

4) RUTH'S MOTHER-IN-LAW

5) BOAZ LET RUTH GATHER GRAIN IN HIS MANY _____.

6) OPPOSITE OF BEGIN

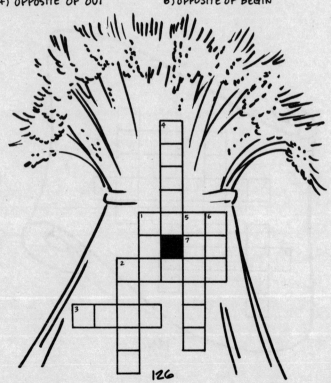

126

YOUNG SAMUEL

AND ELI

I SAMUEL 1:24 – 2:21

ACROSS

1) SAMUEL HAD 3 BROTHERS AND 2 _____.

2) 365 DAYS

7) WHAT A CAT SAYS

DOWN

3) THE PRIEST WHO TOOK CARE OF SAMUEL

4) A JACKET

5) SAMUEL GOT BIGGER, HE _____.

6) HANNAH'S FIRST SON

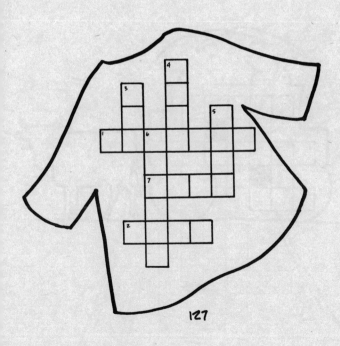

127

THE ARK STOLEN!

1 SAMUEL 4-6

ACROSS

1) A LARGE CART PULLED BY ANIMALS

2) LARGE, STRONG CATTLE

3) TO BE FULL OF FEAR

4) _____ OF THE COVENANT

DOWN

5) HAPPY - RHYMES WITH "PLAID"

6) TO MOVE THE HEAD UP AND DOWN, RHYMES WITH "GOD"

7) NOT CLOSE - RHYMES WITH "CAR"

SAUL, A KING FOR ISRAEL

I SAMUEL 8-10

ACROSS

1) SAM IS SHORT FOR THE NAME _____.

2) YOU MAKE A SANDWICH WITH TWO SLICES OF _____.

3) A MALE RULER OF A COUNTRY. SAUL WAS ISRAEL'S FIRST ____.

DOWN

1) THE MEN ____ A SONG WITH THEIR VOICES.

4) OPPOSITE OF UNDER

5) SAMUEL POURED OIL ON TOP OF SAUL'S ____ TO ANOINT HIM.

6) ISRAEL'S FIRST KING

7) THEY BURNED ____ IN THEIR LAMPS.

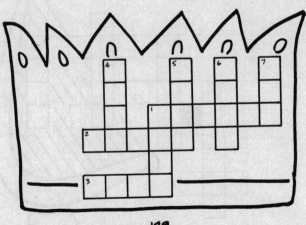

YOUNG DAVID I SAMUEL 16

ACROSS

1) DAVID PLAYED _____ ON HIS HARP. (RHYMES WITH "THONGS")

2) DAVID HAD HOW MANY BROTHERS? (THE NUMBER AFTER SIX)

3) OPPOSITE OF STOP

4) THE STRINGED INSTRUMENT THAT DAVID PLAYED

5) SAMUEL POURED _____ ON DAVID'S HEAD TO ANOINT HIM.

DOWN

6) OPPOSITE OF OLD

7) DAVID WAS A SHEPHERD OVER HIS FATHER'S FLOCK OF _____.

8) DAVID WOULD PLAY SOOTHING MUSIC FOR KING _____.

9) GOD CHOSE _____ TO BE KING AFTER SAUL.

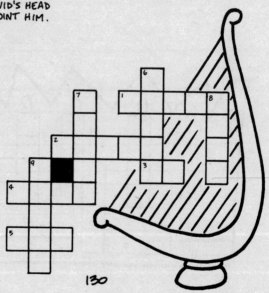

130

DAVID AND JONATHAN
I SAMUEL 18:1-4

ACROSS

1) _____ AND ARROW

2) SAUL'S SON

3) JONATHAN AND DAVID WERE BEST _____.

4) JONATHAN'S FATHER

DOWN

1) DAVID AND JONATHAN LOVED EACH OTHER AS IF THEY WERE _____.

5) MEN SHAKE _____ WHEN THEY FIRST MEET. (RHYMES WITH "SANDS")

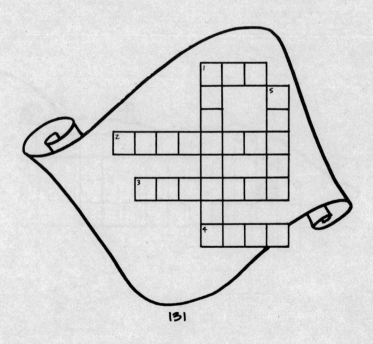

131

DAVID FLEES SAUL 1 SAMUEL 19

ACROSS

1) KING _____ WAS
   ANGRY WITH DAVID

2) OPPOSITE OF SWEET

3) OPPOSITE OF LOVED

4) SAUL BECAME AN
   _____ OF DAVID'S,
   A FOE.

DOWN

5) "_____ AND SEEK"

6) DAVID TRIED TO
   GET FAR _____
   FROM ANGRY SAUL.

7) DAVID _____ AWAY
   FROM KING SAUL

8) OPPOSITE OF HAPPY

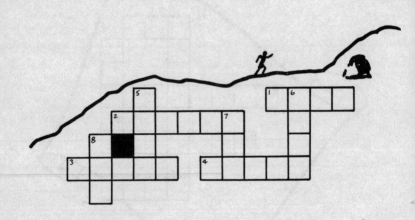

132

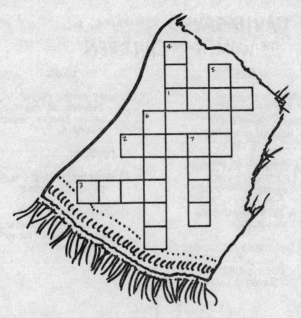

DAVID SPARES SAUL 1 SAMUEL 24

ACROSS

1) STOLE (RHYMES WITH "BOOK")

2) A PART (RHYMES WITH "NIECE")

3) DAVID DID NOT WANT TO HURT KING _____.

DOWN

4) DAVID _____ OFF A PIECE OF KING SAUL'S ROYAL ROBE WITH A KNIFE.

5) KING SAUL WORE A _____ (LIKE "BATA_____").

6) DAVID COULD HAVE _____ KING SAUL, BUT HE DIDN'T.

7) KING SAUL WENT INTO A _____ IN A MOUNTAIN. (RHYMES WITH "SAVE")

133

DAVID SAVES
THE WOMEN AND CHILDREN

I SAMUEL 30

ACROSS

1) OPPOSITE OF HUSBANDS

2) DAVID SAVED EVERY WOMAN AND CHILD, _____ OF THEM.

3) A STICK TO HELP STEADY A PERSON'S WALK (RHYMES WITH "LANE")

4) A VERY SMALL BODY OF WATER

5) DAVID AND HIS MEN _____ ALL THE EVIL KIDNAPPERS, TOOK THEIR LIVES.

DOWN

3) SOME OF THE ENEMY ESCAPED ON THESE HUMP-BACKED DESERT ANIMALS.

5) CHILDREN

6) WHEN PEOPLE ARE STOLEN BY OTHER PEOPLE

7) DAVID AND HIS ARMY _____ THE WOMEN AND CHILDREN (RHYMES WITH "PAVED").

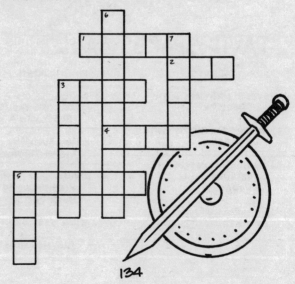

134

KING DAVID

2 SAMUEL 5:1-5

ACROSS

1) DAVID BECAME KING AFTER KING _____ DIED.

2) DAVID CRIED WHEN HE HEARD OF THE DEATH OF HIS BEST _____, JONATHAN.

3) HOW MANY TRIBES IN THE NATION OF ISRAEL?

4) NOW ISRAEL WOULD BE RULED BY _____, THE NEW KING.

DOWN

1) OPPOSITE OF HAPPY

5) A KING WEARS THIS ON HIS HEAD.

6) OPPOSITE OF BEGIN

7) A MAN WHO RULES OVER A COUNTRY (RHYMES WITH "RING")

8) A DEEP HOLE IN THE GROUND WHERE WATER CAN BE DRAWN.

DAVID BRINGS PEACE 2 SAMUEL 8,9

ACROSS

1) OPPOSITE OF SAD

2) LONG BATTLES BETWEEN NATIONS

3) A BUILDING THAT PEOPLE LIVE IN (RHYMES WITH "MOUSE")

4) OPPOSITE OF DOWN

DOWN

5) NO WARS OR FIGHTING

6) DAVID WAS VICTORIOUS AND _____ THE WARS HE FOUGHT.

7) DAVID TOOK CARE OF JONATHAN'S SON, AS HE PROMISED KING _____ THAT HE WOULD (RHYMES WITH "PAUL").

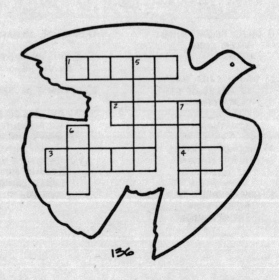

136

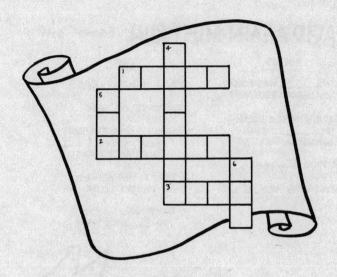

NATHAN AND DAVID   2 SAMUEL 12:1-14

ACROSS

1) REMORSEFUL, TO FEEL
REGRET - RHYMES
WITH "GLORY"

2) THE PROPHET WHO
SHOWED DAVID
HIS SIN

3) IT WAS WRONG FOR
KING DAVID TO ____
ANOTHER MAN'S WIFE.
(RHYMES WITH "LAKE")

DOWN

4) ONE WHO SPEAKS FOR
GOD. NATHAN WAS
A _____.

5) TO DISOBEY GOD -
RHYMES WITH "FIN"

6) NATHAN MADE DAVID
____ (LOOK AT) HIS
OWN GREAT SIN.

137

DAVID AGAIN MUST RUN   2 SAMUEL 15:13-30

ACROSS

1) KING _____ WAS FORCED
   TO LEAVE JERUSALEM.

2) DAVID'S MEN OF WAR,
   OR _____, LEFT
   WITH HIM.

3) RIPPED, SHREDDED

4) HUSBANDS AND _____

DOWN

1) DRY, BARREN LAND

2) OPPOSITE OF FAST

5) DAVID'S SON, ABSALOM,
   MADE HIMSELF _____,
   RULER OVER ISRAEL.

6) PEOPLE WHO SERVED
   IN DAVID'S HOUSE.

7) DAVID WAS FORCED
   TO _____ HIS HOME.

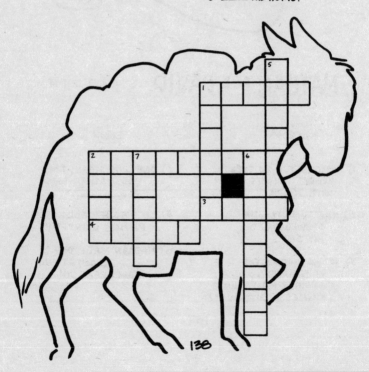

138

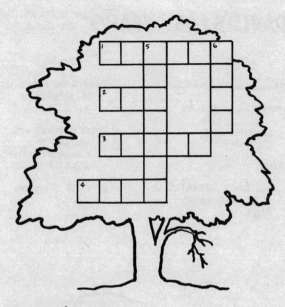

DAVID'S SON, ABSALOM, DIES

2 SAMUEL 18

ACROSS

1) A STAND OF MANY TREES

2) DAVID'S ARMY WAS VICTORIOUS. THEY _____ THE BATTLE.

3) WEPT

4) ABSALOM'S HAIR WAS VERY _____, NOT SHORT.

DOWN

5) DAVID COULD SEE THE MESSENGERS _____ QUICKLY TOWARDS HIM.

6) ABSALOM GOT HIS HAIR CAUGHT IN THE BRANCHES OF A _____.

DAVID'S LAST YEARS

2 SAMUEL 24
1 KINGS 1

ACROSS

1) WE _____ ON CHAIRS

2) NUMERAL, SUCH AS
   _____ ONE.
   (RHYMES WITH
   "LUMBER")

3) ROCK

4) KING DAVID WORSHIPED
   _____ AND LOVED
   HIM.

DOWN

5) SACRIFICES WOULD
   BE OFFERED ON
   AN _____.

6) DAVID ORDERED HIS
   HELPERS TO _____
   HOW MANY MEN
   WERE IN ISRAEL.

7) OPPOSITE OF YOUNG

140

KING SOLOMON

I KINGS 2:1-11

ACROSS

1) THE NATION SOLOMON RULED OVER

2) A KING _____ ON HIS THRONE (RHYMES WITH "FITS").

3) SOLOMON WAS A _____ MAN, NOT OLD.

DOWN

4) DAVID _____ SOON AFTER SOLOMON WAS MADE KING. (OPPOSITE OF LIVED)

5) THE NUMBER AFTER NINETEEN

6) OPPOSITE OF WOMAN

7) SOLOMON WAS DAVID AND BATHSHEBA'S _____ .

ONE BABY
TWO MOTHERS

1 KINGS 3:16-28

ACROSS

1) TO DIVIDE SOMETHING USING A SHARP BLADE - RHYMES WITH "HUT"

2) TO BE VERY WISE IS TO HAVE _____.

3) TO CUT INTO PIECES - RHYMES WITH "ASIDE"

4) OPPOSITE OF FROM

DOWN

1) OFFSPRING - RHYMES WITH "WILD"

5) THE NUMBER AFTER THE NUMBER ONE

6) WHEN SOMETHING IS BOUGHT, IT IS _____ (RHYMES WITH "GOLD").

7) OPPOSITE OF FATHER

8) OPPOSITE OF OUT

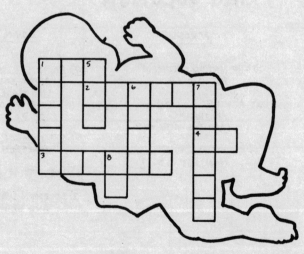

142

QUEEN of SHEBA   1 KINGS 10:1-13

ACROSS

1) QUEEN OF _____

2) A HUMP-BACKED
   DESERT ANIMAL

3) OPPOSITE OF OLD

4) PRECIOUS YELLOW
   METAL

5) WEALTHY

DOWN

1) _____ WAS FULL OF WISDOM.

6) THE _____ OF SHEBA
   VISITED SOLOMON.

7) THE QUEEN OF SHEBA
   CAME FROM A
   _____ AWAY LAND

8) RICHES

143

THE KINGDOM DIVIDES
ISRAEL & JUDAH

I KINGS 12:16-33

ACROSS

1) THE NUMBER THAT FOLLOWS AFTER NINE

2) A MAN WHO RULES A COUNTRY

3) COUNSEL GIVEN TO HELP SOMEONE MAKE A DECISION (ENDS WITH -ICE)

4) ONE OF TWO PARTS (RHYMES WITH "CALF")

DOWN

1) ISRAEL DIVIDED ITS TWELVE _____ INTO TWO KINGDOMS.

5) THE KINGDOM WAS DIVIDED INTO ISRAEL AND _____.

6) THE NEW KINGS DID NOT SEEK _____.

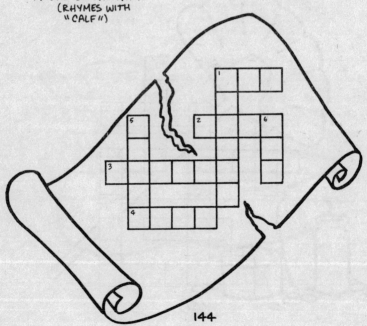

144

ELIJAH RAISES
THE WIDOW'S SON

1 KINGS 17:8-24

ACROSS

1) OPPOSITE OF LAST

2) A WOMAN WHOSE HUSBAND HAS DIED

3) TO TALK TO GOD

DOWN

1) GRAIN GROUND TO A POWDER — RHYMES WITH "HOUR"

4) LAMPS BURN _____ FOR LIGHT.

5) ILL, AILING

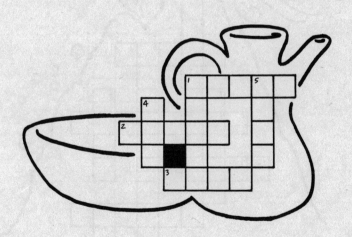

ELIJAH FLEES JEZEBEL   1 KINGS 19:1-18

ACROSS

1) A MESSENGER OF GOD

2) TALL PEAK ON THE LAND

3) STONE

4) FIRE - RHYMES WITH "GAMES"

DOWN

5) TO SWALLOW A LIQUID

6) WHEN THE GROUND SHAKES

7) YOU SPEAK WITH YOUR _____ (RHYMES WITH "CHOICE").

8) THE MOVEMENT OF AIR - RHYMES WITH "PINNED"

9) TO CONSUME FOOD

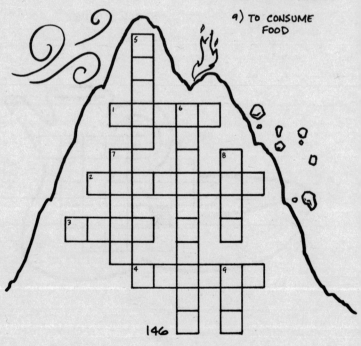

146

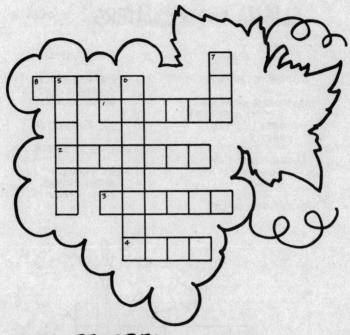

EVIL JEZEBEL   1 KINGS 21

ACROSS

1) JEZEBEL _____ THE
   VINEYARD'S OWNER
   (TOOK HIS LIFE).

2) _____ WAS A
   WICKED WOMAN.

3) RELATIVES

4) _____ CHASE CATS.

8) YOU SLEEP IN A _____.

DOWN

5) THE PROPHET WHO
   THE RAVENS FED

6) A FARM WHERE GRAPES
   ARE GROWN

7) OPPOSITE OF GOOD

147

ELISHA AND THE WATERS   2 KINGS 3

ACROSS

1) OPPOSITE OF TAKE

2) ISRAEL'S ARMY HAD VICTORY OVER MOAB. THEY ___ THE BATTLE.

3) THE LIQUID THAT FLOWS FROM A SPRING

4) OPPOSITE OF LIFE

DOWN

1) THE EARTH UNDER OUR FEET - RHYMES WITH "POUND"

5) ___ AND PEPPER

6) OPPOSITE OF BITTER

7) MORE THAN ONE MAN - RHYMES WITH "TEN"

148

A BOY IS HEALED

2 KINGS
4:8-37

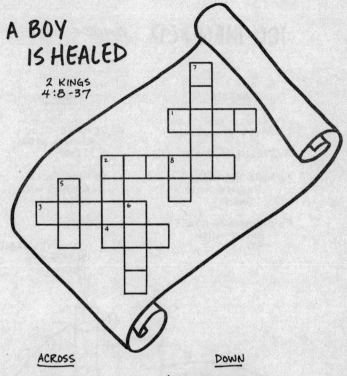

ACROSS

1) ILL

2) OPPOSITE OF MOTHER

3) THE MOTHER _____ HER BOY WITH ALL HER HEART.

4) TO BIND SOMETHING WITH STRING OR ROPE - RHYMES WITH "LIE"

DOWN

2) YOU WEAR SHOES ON THEM

5) OPPOSITE OF GIRL

6) OPPOSITE OF LIVED

7) THE BOY WAS _____ AGAIN! (OPPOSITE OF DEAD)

8) OPPOSITE OF SHE

149

100 MEN FED

2 KINGS 4:42-44

ACROSS

1) LOAVES OF _____

2) OPPOSITE OF WOMEN

3) MORE THAN ENOUGH –
RHYMES WITH
"TWENTY"

4) OPPOSITE OF NONE –
RHYMES WITH
"TALL"

DOWN

2) SEVERAL, ALOT –
RHYMES WITH
"PENNY"

5) TO HAVE EATEN
RHYMES WITH
"PLATE"

6) SPEAK

7) A YELLOW VEGETABLE –
RHYMES WITH
"HORN"

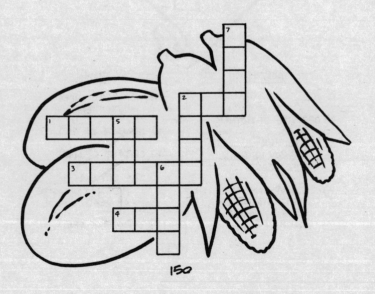

150

THE LOST AXHEAD

2 KINGS 6:1-7

ACROSS

1) THE AXHEAD DROPPED AND _____ INTO THE WATER (RHYMES WITH "WELL").

2) SOMETHING WOODEN IS MADE OF _____.

3) OPPOSITE OF "OUT OF"

4) CLEAR LIQUID FLOWING IN A RIVER

DOWN

1) OPPOSITE OF SINK - RHYMES WITH "BOAT"

5) OPPOSITE OF IN

6) TOOL USED FOR CHOPPING WOOD - RHYMES WITH "TAX"

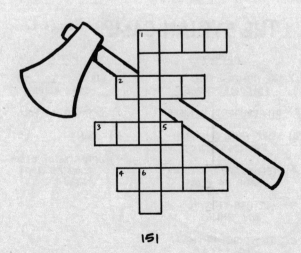

151

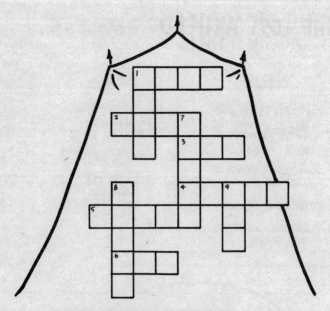

THE SYRIAN CAMP   2 KINGS 7

152

ACROSS

1) THE NUMBER THAT FOLLOWS THREE

2) DISAPPEARED, VANISHED

3) MORE THAN ONE MAN - RHYMES WITH "TEN"

4) TEMPORARY DWELLINGS MADE OF CLOTH

5) WE USE THIS TO BUY THINGS.

6) TO LOOK - RHYMES WITH "TEA"

DOWN

1) WE EAT _____ TO STAY ALIVE.

7) OPPOSITE OF FULL

8) SOUND

9) OPPOSITE OF OLD - RHYMES WITH "FEW"

THE SAMARITANS
AND THE LIONS

2 KINGS 17:24-41

ACROSS

1) LARGE, MANED CATS

2) NATIONS

3) ROADS THROUGH TOWN—
   RHYMES WITH
   "TREATS"

4) LARGE TOWN

DOWN

5) FALSE GODS

6) ONLY A _____
   COULD OFFER
   SACRIFICES OR
   ENTER THE
   TABERNACLE.
   (RHYMES WITH
   "FEAST")

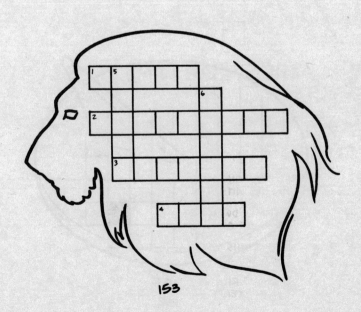

153

HEZEKIAH SPARED

2 KINGS 20:1-11

ACROSS

1) OPPOSITE OF DIE

2) A DEVICE WHICH TELLS TIME USING THE SHADOW CAST BY THE SUN

3) OPPOSITE OF UP

4) TO QUESTION - RHYMES WITH "TASK"

DOWN

5) ILL

6) WHEN WE CRY _____ FALL FROM OUR EYES.

7) THE BRIGHT SUN CASTS THE TREE'S _____ ON THE LAWN. (SHADE CAST BY AN OBJECT)

8) TALK TO GOD

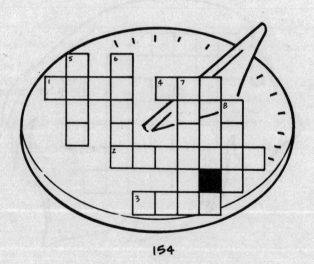

154

KING MANASSEH   2 KINGS 21:1-26

ACROSS

1) FALSE GODS

2) BROKE GOD'S LAW - RHYMES WITH "PINNED"

3) "LIGHT HOLDER" OF THE NIGHT SKY - RHYMES WITH "SOON"

DOWN

2) "LIGHT HOLDER" OF THE DAY - RHYMES WITH "FUN"

4) OPPOSITE OF GOOD

5) MANASSEH _____ MANY INNOCENT PEOPLE (TOOK THEIR LIVES).

6) OPPOSITE OF YES

JEHOSHAPHAT, A GOOD KING

2 CHRONICLES 20:1-21

ACROSS

1) _____ WAS A GOOD KING.

2) A MAN WHO RULES A COUNTRY

3) YOU USE A ____ TO UNLOCK A LOCK.

DOWN

4) THE PEOPLE SANG ____ OF PRAISE TO THE LORD.

5) GRATITUTE

6) JEHOSHAPHAT WOULD ____ TO GOD OFTEN, TALK TO HIM.

7) JEHOSHAPHAT LOVED GOD WITH HIS WHOLE ____.

JOASH RESTORES THE TEMPLE

2 CHRONICLES 24:1-14

ACROSS

1) THE NUMBER AFTER THE NUMBER SIX

2) FIX

3) OPPOSITE OF OLD – RHYMES WITH "FEW"

4) LARGE RECTANGULAR CONTAINER – RHYMES WITH "FOX"

DOWN

5) HOUSE OF WORSHIP

6) THE BOX WAS MADE OF LUMBER, OR _____ (RHYMES WITH "GOOD").

7) OPPOSITE OF OUT

157

KING UZZIAH'S SIN

2 CHRONICLES 26:16-21

ACROSS

1) OPPOSITE OF OUT

2) OPPOSITE OF BEFORE

3) SERIOUS SKIN DISEASE

4) ONLY THE _____ COULD GO INTO THE HOLY PLACE TO BURN THE INCENSE.

DOWN

5) AN AROMATIC SUBSTANCE BURNED FOR FRAGRANCE

6) THE PART OF THE FACE BETWEEN THE EYEBROWS AND HAIRLINE

7) SET APART TO GOD— _____ OF HOLIES

158

REBUILDING THE TEMPLE

EZRA 3:8-13

ACROSS

1) A STRIP OF LEATHER OR CLOTH TIED AROUND THE WAIST.

2) WEPT

3) ROCKS - RHYMES WITH "PHONES"

4) OPPOSITE OF LAST

DOWN

1) ONES WHO BUILD THINGS

5) HAPPY, JOYFUL - RHYMES WITH "HAD"

6) WE ____ ON CHAIRS - RHYMES WITH HIT

159

THE TEMPLE FINISHED   EZRA 6:13-18

ACROSS

1) SET APART TO GOD —
   _____ OF HOLIES

2) TO COMPLETE, TO
   GET DONE

3) THE NUMBER
   BEFORE
   THREE

DOWN

4) OPPOSITE OF BEGIN

5) THOSE WHO SPEAK FOR
   GOD — HAGGAI AND
   ZECHARIAH WERE _____.

6) HAPPINESS, GREAT GLADNESS

7) PRECIOUS YELLOW METAL

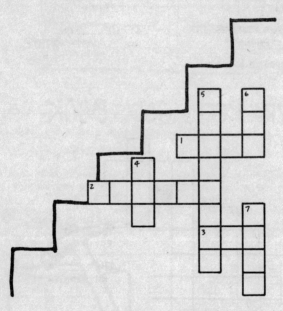

160

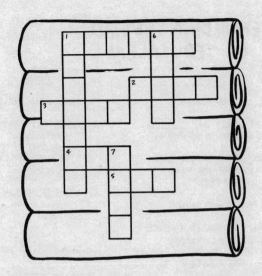

EZRA KEEPS GOD'S BOOK
EZRA

ACROSS

1) ONE WHO COPIED BOOKS AND DID THE JOB OF WRITING THINGS DOWN - RHYMES WITH "BRIBE"

2) DUPLICATE, REPRODUCTION RHYMES WITH "POPPY"

3) SET APART TO GOD - _____ OF HOLIES

4) A RULE, A STATUTE RHYMES WITH "PAW"

5) OPPOSITE OF NEW

DOWN

1) ROLLS WHICH HAVE BEEN WRITTEN ON - RHYMES WITH "ROLLS"

6) MANY PAGES BOUND TOGETHER IS A _____ - RHYMES WITH "COOK"

7) "THE _____ OF GOD" - RHYMES WITH HEARD

161

REBUILDING THE WALLS OF JERUSALEM

NEHEMIAH 2-5

ACROSS

1) _____ AND ARROW

2) THE WALLS OF _____ NEEDED TO BE REBUILT

3) TO GET DOWN ON YOUR KNEES - RHYMES WITH "FEEL"

4) OPPOSITE OF NIGHT

5) AN OPENING IN A FENCE OR WALL THROUGH WHICH TO WALK - RHYMES WITH "DATE"

6) A LARGE TOWN

DOWN

7) ONES WHO BUILD

8) TALL, FLAT STRUCTURES SURROUNDING ANCIENT CITIES - RHYMES WITH "CALLS"

9) OPPOSITE OF DAY

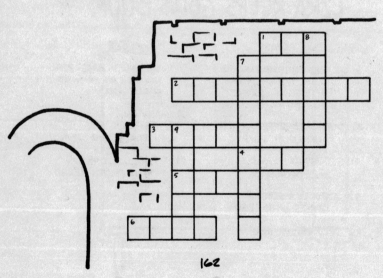

162

EZRA READS THE LAW

NEHEMIAH 8, 13

ACROSS

1) OPPOSITE OF PUSH

2) THE PEOPLE MADE A _____ TO GOD (A VOW).

3) _____ READ THE LAW TO THE PEOPLE.

DOWN

1) HUMAN BEINGS, NATION, RACE – RHYMES WITH "STEEPLE"

4) OPPOSITE OF SAD

5) A TALL STAND FROM WHICH A SPEAKER TALKS

6) OPPOSITE OF WORK – RHYMES WITH "BEST"

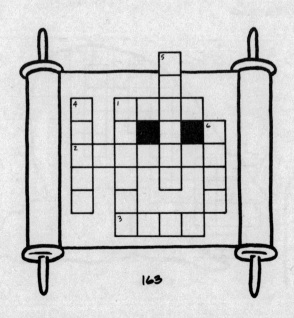

163

THE EVIL HAMAN

ESTHER 3

ACROSS

1) OPPOSITE OF LOVE

2) YOU WEAR A _____ ON YOUR HEAD (RHYMES WITH "CAT").

3) OPPOSITE OF UP

4) A RULE, DECREE, STATUTE - RHYMES WITH "PAW"

DOWN

1) _____ HATED THE JEWS (RHYMES WITH "CANAAN").

3) OPPOSITE OF MOM

5) MORDECAI _____ BY THE GATE EVERY DAY (RHYMES WITH "CAT").

6) CHILDREN OF ISRAEL, HEBREWS

7) HAMAN DEMANDED THAT EVERYONE _____ DOWN TO HIM (RHYMES WITH "HOW").

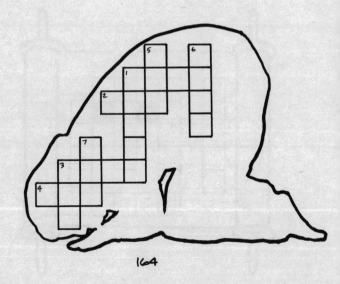

ESTHER TELLS
OF
HAMAN'S PLOT

ACROSS

1) ESTHER _____ HER PEOPLE FROM HAMAN'S EVIL PLOT (RHYMES WITH "PAVED").

2) _____ WAS GOING TO KILL THE JEWS.

3) OPPOSITE OF HIM

4) THE CHILDREN OF ISRAEL, HEBREWS

DOWN

5) GOD USED QUEEN _____ TO SAVE THE JEWS.

6) A LARGE MEAL LATER IN THE DAY - RHYMES WITH "THINNER"

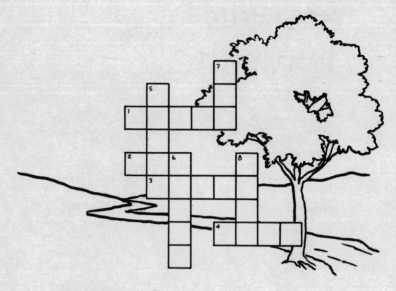

PSALM 1

ACROSS

1) OPPOSITE OF SAD

2) THE NUMBER AFTER NINE

3) LONG, FLOWING BODY OF WATER - RHYMES WITH "QUIVER"

4) A UNIT OF FOLIAGE OF A PLANT - RHYMES WITH "THIEF"

DOWN

5) LIQUID THAT FLOWS IN A RIVER

6) OPPOSITE OF DAY

7) OPPOSITE OF NIGHT

8) VERY TALL PLANT WITH A TRUNK - RHYMES WITH "FREE"

PSALM 42

ACROSS

1) WE EAT ____ TO LIVE.

2) ____ FLOWS OUT OF A FOUNTAIN.

3) WITHOUT WATER TO DRINK YOU HAVE ____ (RHYMES WITH "FIRST")

DOWN

3) ____ FALL FROM OUR EYES WHEN WE CRY.

4) WATER SHOOTING UP OR OUT - RHYMES WITH "MOUNTAIN"

5) A GRACEFUL ANIMAL WITH ANTLERS - RHYMES WITH "FEAR"

6) SMALL RIVER OR BROOK - RHYMES WITH "CREAM"

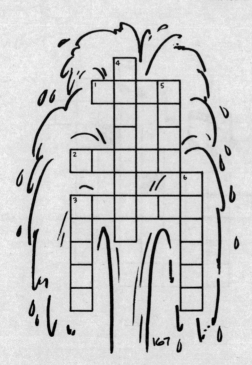

167

PSALM 117

ACROSS

1) OPPOSITE OF HERS

2) "PRAISE THE _____"

3) TO WORSHIP, ADORE, EXTOL - RHYMES WITH "RAISE"

4) "_____ THY MOTHER AND THY FATHER"

DOWN

5) BENEVOLENCE, THE QUALITY OF BEING KIND

6) ETERNITY

7) OPPOSITE OF HER

8) OPPOSITE OF LIE

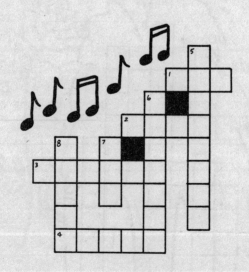

168

THE VIRTUOUS WOMAN

PROVERBS 31:10-31

ACROSS

1) LABORS, EFFORTS, TASKS
   RHYMES WITH "PERKS"

2) THE LIMBS THAT EXTEND
   FROM THE SHOULDERS

3) OPPOSITE OF BAD

4) "CLAP YOUR ____."
   RHYMES WITH
   "SANDS"

5) A WOMAN IS MARRIED
   TO HER _____.

DOWN

1) OPPOSITE OF MAN

4) A BUILDING
   PEOPLE LIVE IN

6) OPPOSITE OF
   WEAK

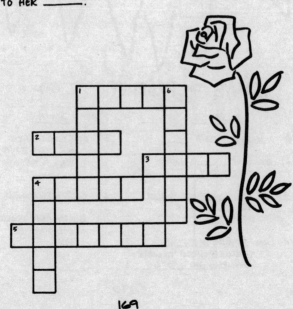

169

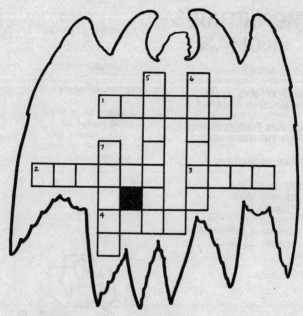

ISAIAH the PROPHET

ISAIAH 6

ACROSS

1) A KING SITS ON A _____.

2) GOD GAVE _____ A VISION OF PROPHESY.

3) WE SPEAK WITH OUR TONGUE AND ____ (RHYMES WITH "SIPS").

4) AN OPENING IN A FENCE THROUGH WHICH TO WALK - RHYMES WITH "LATE"

DOWN

5) ONE WHO SPEAKS FOR GOD; ISAIAH WAS A GREAT _____.

6) GOD'S MESSENGERS

7) BIRDS AND ANGELS USE THESE TO FLY.

THE SOARING EAGLE

ISAIAH 40:31

ACROSS

1) THE SPACE OVERHEAD, THE HEAVENS - RHYMES WITH "FLY"

2) TO MOVE AS FAST AS YOU CAN BY FOOT - RHYMES WITH "FUN"

3) THE FINAL AIM IN A CONTEST, TO GET A POINT - RHYMES WITH "SOUL"

4) OPPOSITE OF WEAK

DOWN

1) TO RISE UP HIGH, "_____ LIKE AN EAGLE" - RHYMES WITH "POOR"

5) BIRDS FLAP THEIR _____.

6) THE OPPOSITE ONE OF TWO - "NOT THAT ONE. THE _____ ONE."

7) "PRAISE THE _____."

8) LARGE BIRD OF PREY, SYMBOL OF THE USA

171

JEREMIAH IN PRISON

ACROSS

1) TO TALK, TO UTTER SPEECH - RHYMES WITH "PEAK"

2) OPPOSITE OF SHE

3) OPPOSITE OF UP

4) A PLACE WHERE PEOPLE ARE HELD CAPTIVE, A DUNGEON - RHYMES WITH "RISEN"

DOWN

4) A DEEP HOLE IN THE GROUND - RHYMES WITH "PIT"

5) _____ WAS THROWN IN PRISON.

6) FALSE GODS

7) OPPOSITE OF OFF

172

EZEKIEL'S VISION
EZEKIEL 37:1-14

<u>ACROSS</u>

1) OPPOSITE OF FOUND

2) THE LOWLAND BETWEEN TWO MOUNTAINS - RHYMES WITH "GALLEY"

3) ONLY A _____ COULD OFFER SACRIFICES TO THE LORD.

4) THE PARTS OF OUR SKELETON - RHYMES WITH "STONES"

<u>DOWN</u>

5) OPPOSITE OF DEAD

6) GOD GAVE _____ A VISION.

7) ANTICIPATION OF A GOOD THING - RHYMES WITH "SOAP"

173

DANIEL AND THE KING'S DREAM

ACROSS

1) YOU WEAR SHOES ON YOUR _____.

2) THE PLATE _____ WHEN I DROPPED IT.- RHYMES WITH "JOKE"

3) _____ COULD TELL THE MEANINGS OF THE KING'S DREAMS.

4) THE COLOR OF CLAY - RHYMES WITH "PLAY"

5) A PRECIOUS METAL - WE USE _____ WARE TO EAT WITH.

DOWN

4) PRECIOUS YELLOW METAL

6) ROCK

7) A VISION DURING SLEEP

8) A THICK, MOLDABLE SUBSTANCE, CAN BE FIRED TO MAKE POTTERY - RHYMES WITH "GRAY"

9) TO HAVE EATEN - RHYMES WITH "PLATE"

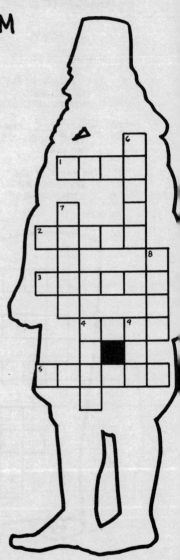

174

DANIEL AND THE LIONS

DANIEL 6

ACROSS

1) OPPOSITE OF CLOSED

2) THE LIONS DID NOT HARM _____.

3) AN OPENING THROUGH THE WALL TO THE OUTSIDE TO LET IN LIGHT AND FRESH AIR.

4) TO GET DOWN ON YOUR KNEES - RHYMES WITH "FEEL"

DOWN

5) A CAVE WHERE THE LIONS LIVED - RHYMES WITH "PEN"

6) TO TALK TO GOD

7) OPPOSITE OF MANY

8) KINGS OF BEASTS

9) A FEMALE DEER

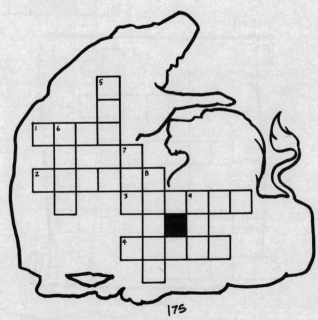

ZACHARIAS

LUKE 1:5-25

ACROSS

1) A MESSENGER OF GOD, GABRIEL, THE _____

2) _____ THE BAPTIST

3) KIDS

4) ZACHARIAS WAS A _____ WHO SERVED IN THE TEMPLE (RHYMES WITH "FEAST").

DOWN

5) FOR A TIME ZACHARIAS COULD NOT _____ (TALK).

6) AN ANGEL APPEARED TO _____ (JOHN THE BAPTIST'S FATHER).

7) OPPOSITE OF YOUNG

8) A BOY CHILD - RHYMES WITH "FUN" OPPOSITE OF DAUGHTER

176

MARY VISITS ELIZABETH

LUKE 1:39-45

ACROSS

1) THE CHILD OF ONE'S UNCLE OR AUNT - RHYMES WITH "DOZEN"

2) MARY WENT TO VISIT HER COUSIN_____.

3) GLADNESS, GREAT HAPPINESS

4) ELIZABETH WOULD HAVE A _____ BOY (RHYMES WITH "MAYBE")

DOWN

5) TO GO SEE SOMEONE FOR A SHORT STAY

6) THE MOTHER OF JESUS

7) SET APART TO GOD, _____ OF HOLIES

177

THE ANGELS
TELL THE SHEPHERDS

LUKE 2:8-20

ACROSS

1) GREAT GLADNESS, HAPPINESS

2) THOSE WHO CARE FOR SHEEP

3) "GLORY TO _____ IN THE HIGHEST"

DOWN

1) _____ WAS THE NEWBORN SAVIOR.

2) TO LOOK WITH YOUR EYES - RHYMES WITH "BEE"

4) GOD'S MESSENGERS

5) OPPOSITE OF DAY

6) FEARFUL

7) THE SPACE HIGH OVERHEAD, THE HEAVENS - RHYMES WITH "PIE"

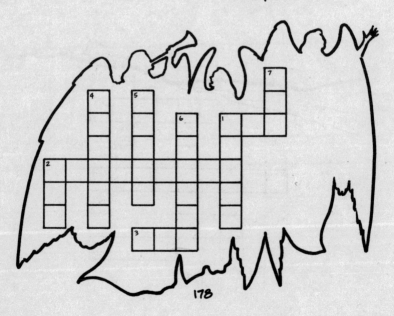

178

THE WISE MEN

MATTHEW 2:1-12

ACROSS

1) PRECIOUS YELLOW METAL

2) OPPOSITE OF WEST

3) IF YOU HAVE WISDOM, YOU ARE _____.

4) PRESENTS

5) MOTHER OF JESUS

6) THE MAN WHO RULES OVER A COUNTRY

DOWN

5) OPPOSITE OF WOMEN

7) THE BUILDING PEOPLE LIVE IN - RHYMES WITH "MOUSE"

8) HUMP-BACKED DESERT CREATURES

9) SMALL CITY - RHYMES WITH "DOWN"

10) BRIGHT POINT OF LIGHT IN THE NIGHT SKY

11) THE SPACE OVERHEAD, THE HEAVENS - RHYMES WITH "PIE"

179

JESUS AS A BOY

LUKE 2:39-40

ACROSS

1) AN ANGEL TOLD JOSEPH TO ___ BACK TO ISRAEL (OPPOSITE OF STOP).

2) IF YOU HAVE WISDOM, YOU ARE _____ (RHYMES WITH "EYES").

3) OPPOSITE OF GIRL

4) FATHER, SON, HOLY _____

DOWN

1) GOT BIGGER

3) A CREATURE WITH FEATHERS AND WINGS

5) THE SON OF GOD

6) THE LAND WHERE PHARAOHS RULED - MOSES LED THE PEOPLE OUT OF _____ .

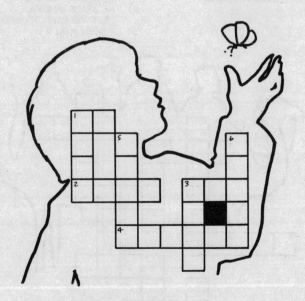

JOHN the BAPTIST

LUKE 3:1-11

ACROSS

1) A DRY, BARREN LAND

2) _____ THE BAPTIST

3) TO TURN AWAY FROM SIN AND DO RIGHT- RHYMES WITH "RESENT"

4) OPPOSITE OF SHE

DOWN

5) JOHN WORE CLOTHES MADE OF ANIMAL _____ (RHYMES WITH "THIN").

6) ONE WHO SPEAKS FOR GOD

7) JOHN ATE LOCUSTS AND WILD _____ (THE SWEET SYRUP BEES MAKE).

JESUS IN THE DESERT

MATTHEW 4:1-11

ACROSS

1) ROCKS

2) SATAN IS THE _____.
   (RHYMES WITH
   "LEVEL")

3) _____ WAS TEMPTED
   IN THE DESERT.

4) SATAN SAID, "IF YOU
   ARE THE SON OF GOD,
   MAKE THESE STONES
   INTO LOAVES OF _____."

DOWN

2) A BARREN, DRY
   LAND

5) THERE IS ONLY _____
   GOD (THE NUMBER
   BEFORE TWO).

6) WICKED, BAD

7) OPPOSITE OF SIT -
   RHYMES WITH
   "HAND"

PETER, PHILIP AND NATHANAEL

ACROSS

1) ONES WHO FOLLOW

2) GOD'S DWELLING PLACE ON HIGH

3) MORE THAN ONE MAN - OPPOSITE OF WOMEN

4) OPPOSITE OF OFF

DOWN

1) JESUS NOW HAD _____ FOLLOWERS (THE NUMBER AFTER FOUR).

5) TO PLACE YOUR FAITH IN SOMETHING - "I _____ IN GOD." (RHYMES WITH "RELIEVE")

6) OPPOSITE OF CLOSED

7) A VERY TALL PLANT WITH A TRUNK - RHYMES WITH "FREE"

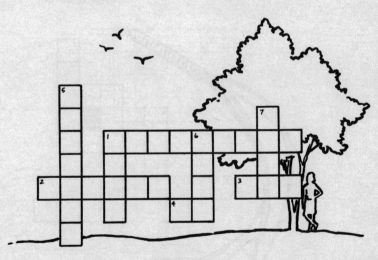

183

JESUS CLEANS OUT THE TEMPLE

JOHN 2:12-16

ACROSS

1) THE NUMBER AFTER NINE

2) TO PURCHASE - RHYMES WITH "MY"

3) HOUSE OF WORSHIP

4) OPPOSITE OF BUY

DOWN

1) FLAT PIECES OF FURNITURE ON LEGS- RHYMES WITH "CABLES"

5) WE USE _____ TO BUY THINGS

6) A LION TAMER USES A _____ AND A CHAIR TO CONTROL THE LIONS (RHYMES WITH "RIP")

7) ANGRY

8) OPPOSITE OF IN

184

HEROD PUTS JOHN IN PRISON

LUKE 3:18-20

ACROSS

1) KING HEROD PUT JOHN THE BAPTIST IN A PRISON FAR _____.

2) OPPOSITE OF LOVED

3) _____ THE BAPTIST

DOWN

2) KING _____ RULED OVER GALILEE.

4) A MAN IS MARRIED TO HIS _____.

5) OPPOSITE OF NO

6) TO USE YOUR BRAIN, MEDITATE - RHYMES WITH "DRINK"

185

THE NOBLEMAN'S SON

JOHN 4:46-54

ACROSS

1) THERE ARE 24 OF THESE IN ONE DAY, 60 MINUTES IS ONE _____.

2) AN IMPORTANT, RICH MAN OF HIGH RANK

3) THE SON OF GOD

DOWN

1) CURED

4) OPPOSITE OF DAUGHTER, A BOY CHILD

5) WHEN A PERSON IS HOT FROM AN ILLNESS, HE HAS A _____.

6) STREETS, WELL-TRAVELED PATHS - RHYMES WITH "TOADS"

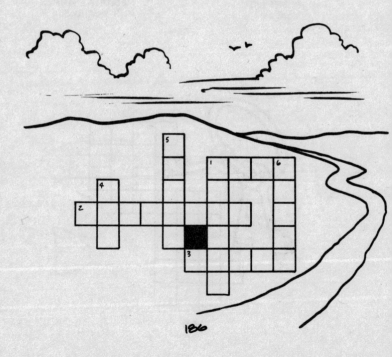

186

THE FISHERMEN

LUKE 5:1-11

ACROSS

1) A LARGE BODY OF WATER - RHYMES WITH "TEA"

2) A WEB OF CORD FISHERMAN USE TO CATCH FISH - RHYMES WITH "PET"

3) OPPOSITE OF EMPTY

4) VESSELS TO CARRY MEN ON WATER - RHYMES WITH "COATS"

DOWN

3) FINNED CREATURES THAT LIVE IN WATER

5) OPPOSITE OF FEW

6) ONE LESS THAN THREE

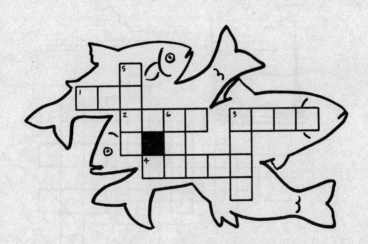

187

THROUGH THE ROOF

LUKE 5:17-26

ACROSS

1) THE TOP OF A HOUSE

2) AN OWL ASKS, "____?".

3) CURED

4) TO BREAK GOD'S LAW

8) PLACE, LOCATION
"_____ WERE
YOU BORN?" -
RHYMES WITH "HAIR"

DOWN

2) TO STROLL - TRAVEL
BY FOOT - RHYMES
WITH "TALK"

5) LARGE GROUP OF
PEOPLE - RHYMES
WITH "LOUD"

6) TO PARDON -
ENDS WITH "GIVE"

7) WE SLEEP IN A ____.

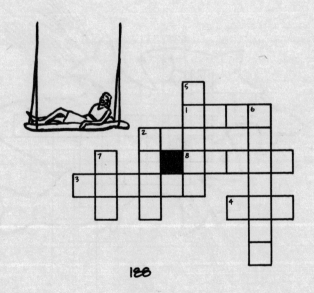

188

JESUS, LORD
OF
THE SABBATH

MATTHEW 12:1-13

ACROSS

1) OPPOSITE OF SHE

2) THE SEEDS OF CEREAL PLANTS LIKE WHEAT - RHYMES WITH "TRAIN"

3) DEEP HOLE IN THE GROUND - RHYMES WITH "SIT"

4) RULE, STATUTE - RHYMES WITH "PAW"

5) WE HAVE A _____ AT THE END OF EACH ARM.

DOWN

1) WHEN YOU DON'T EAT, YOU GET _____.

6) THE LORD'S DAY, DAY OF REST

7) FARMERS GROW CROPS IN THEIR _____.

8) TO HAVE EATEN - RHYMES WITH "GATE"

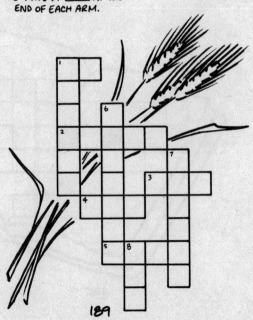

189

THE TWELVE APOSTLES

LUKE 6:12-16

ACROSS

1) OPPOSITE OF FALSE

2) THE TAX COLLECTOR

3) JESUS CHOSE TWELVE
   _____.

4) HIS NAME MEANS
   "ROCK"

DOWN

1) THE NUMBER AFTER
   ELEVEN

5) OPPOSITE OF BOTTOM

6) OPPOSITE OF HERS
   (BELONGING TO HIM)

7) THE APOSTLE WHO
   WOULD BETRAY
   JESUS.

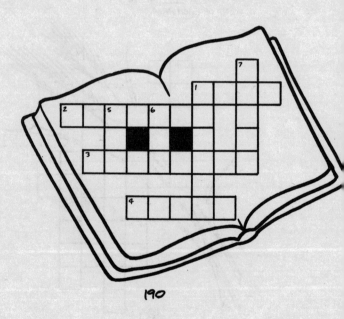

190

THE SOWER

LUKE 8:4-15

ACROSS

1) TO SCATTER SEEDS – RHYMES WITH "TOW"

2) OPPOSITE OF GOOD

3) THE DIRT WE WALK ON, THE EARTH – RHYMES WITH "FOUND"

4) A PLANT GROWS FROM A _____ (RHYMES WITH "FEED").

DOWN

2) WINGED, FEATHERED FLYING CREATURES

3) OPPOSITE OF BAD

5) ROSES HAVE SHARP _____.

6) STONE – RHYMES WITH "CLOCK"

191

PARABLES of JESUS

ACROSS

1) STORIES JESUS TOLD TO SHOW A TRUTH

2) RICHES, VALUABLES - "BURIED _____"

3) THE GRAIN WE MAKE FLOUR FROM - RHYMES WITH "SEAT"

4) A PLANT GROWS FROM A _____ (RHYMES WITH "FEED")

DOWN

5) KETCHUP AND _____ GO GREAT ON A HOT DOG (RHYMES WITH "CUSTARD").

6) A BEAUTIFUL FLOWER WITH THORNS - RHYMES WITH "HOSE"

7) WINGED, FEATHERED FLYING CREATURES

8) A VERY TALL PLANT WITH A TRUNK - RHYMES WITH "FREE"

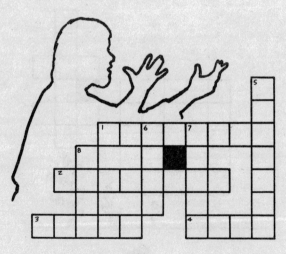

192

A GIRL LIVES AGAIN

MARK 5:35-43

ACROSS

1) THE GIRL'S PARENTS WERE _____ THAT SHE WAS DEAD (OPPOSITE OF HAPPY).

2) NOT ALIVE

3) TO BE IN THE STATE OF SLEEP

4) OPPOSITE OF FALL - JESUS TOLD THE GIRL TO _____ UP (RHYMES WITH EYES).

DOWN

5) JESUS TOOK HER BY THE _____ (RHYMES WITH "SAND").

6) _____ RAISED THE GIRL FROM THE DEAD.

7) SHE WAS _____ YEARS OLD (ONE MORE THAN ELEVEN).

8) ALL THE PEOPLE MADE A LOUD _____ OUTSIDE (OPPOSITE OF LAUGH).

193

JESUS WALKS ON WATER
MATTHEW 14:22-27

ACROSS

1) TRAVELED BY FOOT, STROLLED - RHYMES WITH "TALKED"

2) TO BE AFRAID IS TO BE FULL OF _____. (RHYMES WITH "HEAR")

3) A VIOLENT DISTURBANCE IN THE WEATHER - RHYMES WITH "FORM"

DOWN

1) JESUS WALKED ON _____.

4) TRANSPARENT - THE WATER WAS CRYSTAL _____. (RHYMES WITH "FEAR")

5) THE SON OF GOD

6) A VESSEL THAT CARRIES MEN UPON THE WATER - RHYMES WITH "COAT"

194

JESUS TRANSFIGURED

MARK 9:2-10

ACROSS

1) A TALL PEAK OF LAND

2) GOD SAID, "THIS IS MY BELOVED_____"

3) WHITE FLAKES THAT FALL FROM THE SKY IN WINTER

DOWN

1) THE MAN GOD CHOSE TO LEAD THE PEOPLE OUT OF EGYPT- RHYMES WITH "HOSES"

4) THE DISCIPLE CALLED "THE ROCK"

5) OPPOSITE OF LOW

6) MIDDAY- RHYMES WITH "SOON"

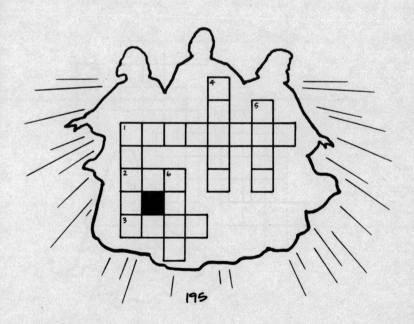

195

MARY AND MARTHA

LUKE 10:38-42

ACROSS

1) OPPOSITE OF UP

2) _____ WAS TOO
   BUSY WORKING.
   (MARY'S SISTER)

3) ACTIVE, DOING MANY
   THINGS — RHYMES
   WITH "DIZZY"

DOWN

2) _____ SAT AT THE
   FEET OF JESUS AND
   LISTENED TO HIS WORDS.
   (MARTHA'S SISTER)

4) TO LABOR, EXERT EFFORT —
   RHYMES WITH "PERK"

5) THE SON OF GOD

6) OPPOSITE OF STAND

196

ANSWERS

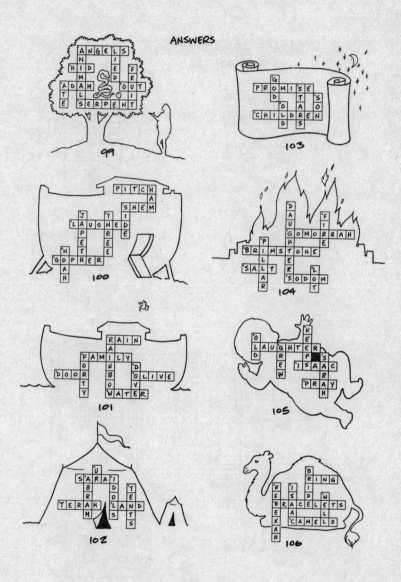

99

ANGELS
A I I
HID E F R
M M E I
ADAM OUT
T L I
E SERPENT

103

G
PROMISE
D
O T S
D A O
CHILDREN R
S

100

PITCH A
SHEM I
J TREE D
LAUGHED E
P E
N E
GOPHER
A
H

104

D F
AU I
PRIMSTONE R E
I U R
SALT G SODOM
L H A
A T L
R SODOM T

101

RAIN
A
FAMILY
O A D
DOOR I O OLIVE
T N L
Y B I
WATER V
E

105

K
O E
LAUGHTER
R P S
E I ISAAC
W A R
PRAY A
H

102

U
SARAI I
B D
R IDOLS
TERAH A T
H L E
A N N
M D T
S

106

B
R
I
REBEKAH I N
I D G
BRACELETS
A W
CAMELS L
S

ANSWERS

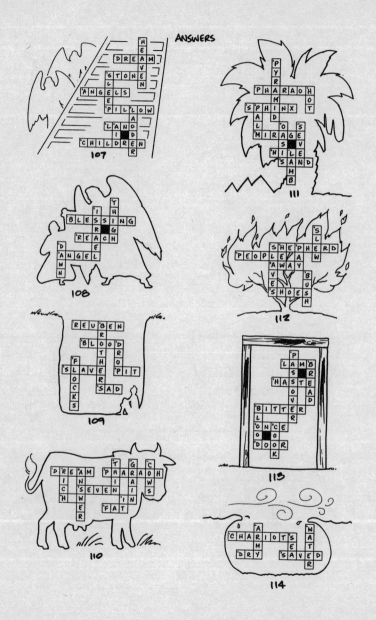

107

HEAVEN
DREAM
STONE / SLEEP
ANGELS
PILLOW / LADDER
LAND
CHILDREN

108

THING
BLESSING / REACH
REACH
DAWN / ANGEL

109

REUBEN / BROTHER
BLOOD / DROP
PIT
FLOCKS / SLAVE
SAD

110

DREAM / RICH
PHARAOH / THIN / GRAIN / COWS
SEVEN
FAT
THIN / POWER

111

PYRAMID
PHARAOH / HOT
SPHINX / DATES
ALADOS
MIRAGE / SAVE
NILE
SAND
LAMB

112

SHEPHERD / SLOW
PEOPLE / WAY
AWAY / BUSH
SAVE
SHOES

113

PASSOVER
LAMB / BREAD
HASTE
BITTER / BLOOD
ONCE / OR
DOOR

114

DAM
CHARIOTS / ARMY / WATER
DRY / SAVED

ANSWERS

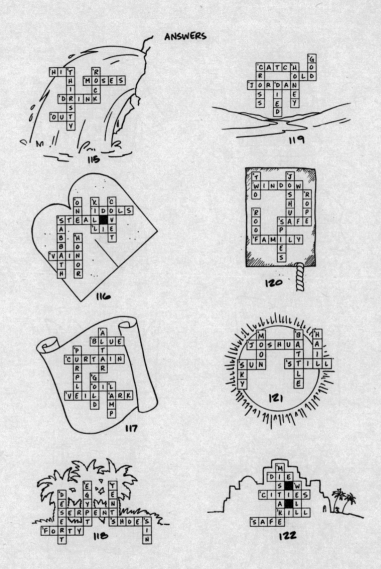

ANSWERS

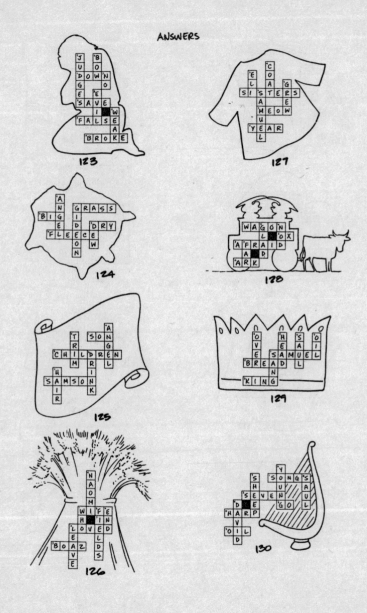

123

124

125

126

127

128

129

130

ANSWERS

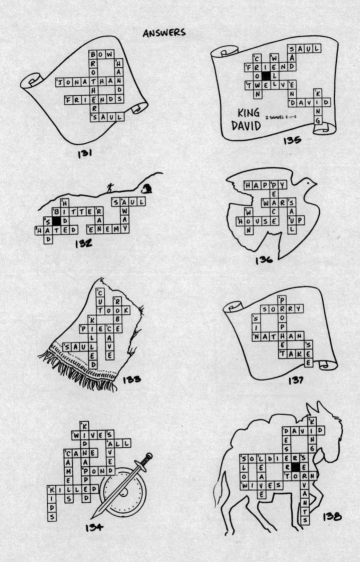

131

135

132

136

133

137

134

138

ANSWERS

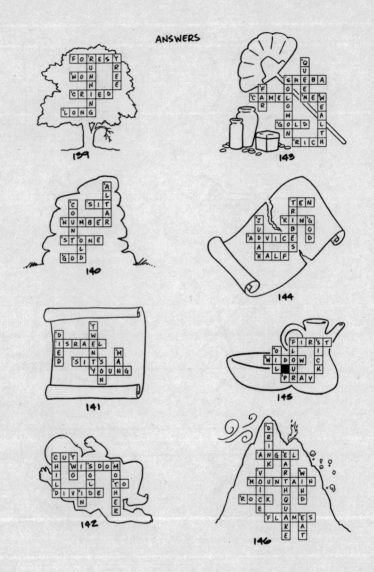

139
FOREST / TREE / WON / RUNNING / CRIED / LONG

140
ALTAR / COW / SIT / GOLD / NUMBER / STONE / GOD

141
TWIN / DIED / ISRAEL / MAN / SIT / ITS / YOUNG

142
CUT / CHILD / WISDOM / WOOL / TO / OTHER / DIVIDE

143
QUEEN / SHEBA / ROOM / CAMEL / LOOM / NEW / WEALTH / GOLD / CON / RICH / FAR

144
TEN / KING / GOD / JUDGE / RIBS / ADVICE / HALF

145
FIRST / OIL / SICK / WIDOW / LOUR / PRAY

146
DRINK / ANGEL / VIE / EARTH / WIND / MOUNTAIN / ROCK / QUAKE / FLAMES / EAT

ANSWERS

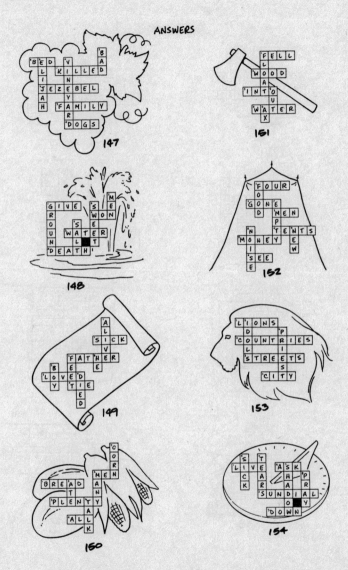

147

Grid reads:
BED / BAD
LIE / KILLED
JEZEBEL
FAMILY
DOGS

151

FELL
WOOD
INTO
WATER
WAX

148

GIVE / MEN
SWON
WATER
DEATH

152

FOUR
GONE
MEN
TENTS
MONEY
SEE
NOISE

149

ALIVE
SICK
FATHER
BELOVED / TIE
DIED

153

LIONS
COUNTRIES
STREETS
CITY

150

CORN
HEN
BREAD
PLENTY
TALK

154

STICK
LIVE / ASK
HARP
SUNDIAL
DOWN

ANSWERS

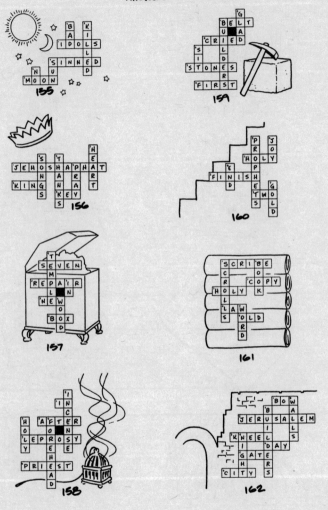

155

BAD
KILLED
IDOLS
SINNED
NU
MOON

159

G
BELT
U
CRIED
A
I
L
STONES
D
E
FIRST
R

156

JEHOSHAPHAT
S
Y
HEART
H
A
A
KINGS
N
R
KEY
K
T
S

160

PRO
HOLY
E
P
FINISH
H
T
E
GOLD
W
L
O
S
D

157

T
SEVEN
M
REPAIR
P
L
L
NEW
E
W
O
BOX
R
D

161

SCRIBE
C
O
R
COPY
O
HOLY
L
K
L
L
LAW
S
OLD
R
D

158

I
N
HAFTER
O
C
O
N
LEPROSY
E
Y
E
E
H
E
A
PRIEST
D

162

BOWL
A
B
JERUSALEM
I
L
KNEEL
L
DAY
I
GATE
R
H
S
CITY

ANSWERS

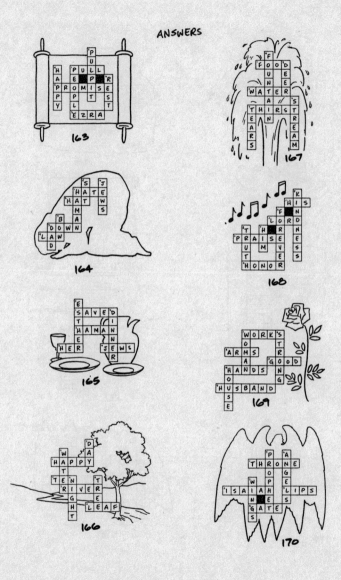

163

P
PULL
HAPPY E P R
PROMISE S E
P L T S
Y L EZRA T

164

S JEWS
HATE E
HAMAN S
B W
DOWN N
LAW D

165

E SAVED
S I
T HAMAN N
HER N
JEWS E
R

166

D
W A
HAPPY
T T
TEN R
RIVER TREE
G L
H LEAF
T

167

F
FOOD
O E
U E
WATER S
A STREAM
THIRST R
E E
TEARS A
R M
S

168

K
HIS
F N
LORD D
T FORE N
PRAISE V E
U M E S
TRUTH R S
H
HONOR

169

WORKS
O T
ARMS R
A GOOD
HANDS N
O G
HUSBAND
E

170

P A
THRONE
R O
O G
WISAIAH LIPS
N E
GATE
S

ANSWERS

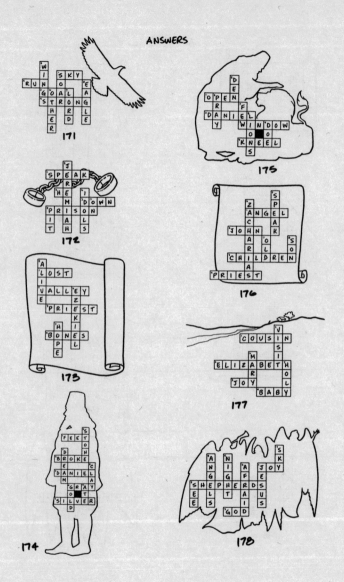

171

WIN
RUN SKY
GOAL
STRONG EAGLE
HER
BIRD

172

SPEAK
JEREMIAH
THEM DOWN
PRISON
IT
H
I
LS

173

A
LOST
RIVER
VALLEY
E Z
PRIEST
K I
HOPE
BONES
E

174

STONE
FEET
BROKE
DANIEL
GRAY
SILVER

175

DEN
OPEN
R F
DANIEL
Y WINDOW
O
KNEEL

176

SPELL
ZANGEL
C
JOHN
R SON
O
CHILDREN
A
PRIEST

177

V
COUSIN
I
M
ELIZABETH
R
JOY
BABY

178

ANGEL
NIGHT
SKY
JOY
AFRAID
JESUS
SHEPHERDS
GOD

ANSWERS

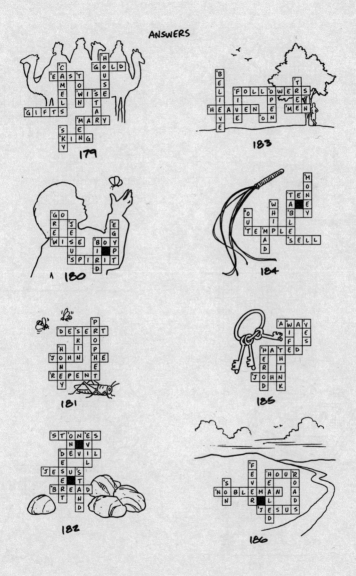

179

C A M E L S
E A S T
G O L D
H O U S E
T O W N
W I S E
S T A R
G I F T S
M A R Y
S K I N G
Y

183

B E L I E V E
F O L L O W E R S
T E M P E R
H E A V E N
O P E N
M E N

180

G O
G R E E T
J E S U S
E G Y P T
W I S E
B O Y
S P I R I T

184

M O N E Y
T A B L E
W H I L E
O U T
T E M P L E
S E L L

181

D E S E R T
P R O P H E T
K I N G
J O H N
R E P E N T

185

A W A Y
W I F E
Y E S
H A T E D
H E R
T H I N G
J O H N

182

S T O N E S
O N E
D E V I L
D E S E
J E S U S
T
B R E A D
N D

186

F E V E R
H O U R
R O A D
S O N
N O B L E M A N
J E S U S
D

ANSWERS

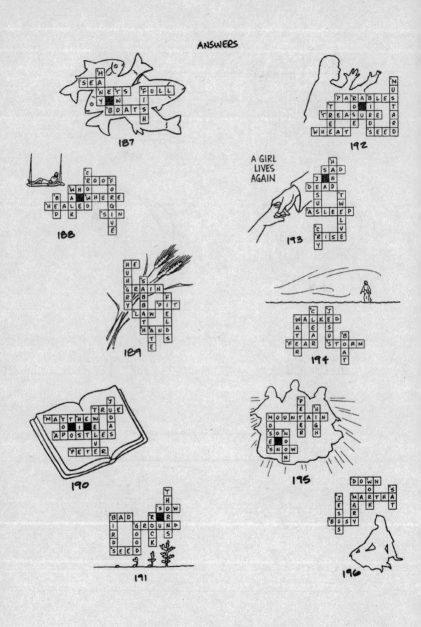